THE HABIT-FORMING GUIDE
TO BECOMING A

Systems Thinker

by Tracy Benson & Sheri Marlin

Published by
Systems Thinking Group
150 Gamma Drive
Pittsburgh, PA 15238
Watersfoundation.org

Graphic Design by AB Graphic Design, www.abgraphicdesign.com

Printed by The Print Room, Tucson, Arizona, www.theprintroom.com

ISBN: 978-0-9978834-1-1

Dedicated to
James and Faith Waters
Our mentors, supporters and sources of inspiration

*Delivering benefits to make the world
a better place for everyone!*

WHAT PEOPLE ARE SAYING ABOUT THE WATERS FOUNDATION AND THE HABITS OF A SYSTEMS THINKER:

"I believe in systems thinking because I've never seen anything that can be so consistently applied. I see it as a toolbox of critical thinking skills that students can use to demonstrate analysis or make their critical thinking visible. Like Batman has his utility belt for whatever problem he's faced with, these kids have these tools."

— David Rifkin, High School Teacher, Hewlett-Woodmere Public Schools, Woodmere, NY

"The Habits of a Systems Thinker are helping educators bring a coherent overall framework to a field that has had many pioneers in various school settings. We are now witnessing that seeing the big picture, identifying circles of causality, understanding how the structure of a system produces its behavior, and recognizing the benefits of looking at problems from different perspectives can help educators focus on deeper thinking skills across virtually all curricula and ages."

— Daniel Goleman, author of *Emotional Intelligence* and co-author with Peter Senge of *The Triple Focus*, morethansound.net

"I've always really valued a classroom where I'm developing critical thinking skills with students who are genuinely engaged. When I use this language of the Habits and these tools with kids, it makes me more excited in my teaching because I start hearing kids who are questioning other students' assumptions in very diplomatic, very grounded ways and conversations really rooted in evidence and curiosity."

— Daniel Murphy-Cairns, Elementary Teacher, Portland, OR

"Systems thinking habits and tools help students articulate their understanding of the systems they are studying. When middle school students have visual tools that assist their learning and encourage them to think deeply about things that matter to them, they become more motivated and engaged. I've been a middle level administrator for 21 years and have not found a better way to improve school culture, address organizational challenges and promote rigor and relevance in classroom instruction."

— Kathy Scheppe, Former Middle School Principal, Currently Director of K-8/Elementary Schools, Tucson Unified School District, AZ

"There is no more difficult task than to take very complex concepts and simplify them so that people of all ages can grasp and apply them. This 20-year effort that produced the Habits of a Systems Thinker shows that the value is clearly worth the investment."

— Peter Senge, best-selling author of *The Fifth Discipline*, senior lecturer at MIT

"The essence of Systems Thinking is understanding relationships and their implications. Developing a formula for doing that is essentially impossible though the Habits of a Systems Thinker are the best possible alternative. The Habits of a Systems Thinker provide alternative perspectives through which one should consider a situation and identify relevant connections that should be included in the relationship map. We seek the path, we find the path, we travel the path, we become the path, and the Habits of a Systems Thinker provide critical components for the 'travel the path' component." — Gene Bellinger, Director, Systems Thinking World Inc.

Seeks to understand the "big picture"

©2014 Waters Foundation, Systems Thinking in Schools
www.watersfoundation.org

Changes perspectives to increase understanding

©2014 Waters Foundation, Systems Thinking in Schools
www.watersfoundation.org

Considers an issue fully and resists the urge to come to a quick conclusion

©2014 Waters Foundation, Systems Thinking in Schools
www.watersfoundation.org

Identifies the circular nature of complex cause and effect relationships

Waters Foundation, Systems Thinking in Schools
www.watersfoundation.org

Observes how elements within systems change over time, generating patterns and trends

oundation, Systems Thinki
www.watersfoundation.org

Surfaces and tests assumptions

Sugar | Vitamins

Super Star Cereal

Foundation, Systems Thinking in Schools
dation.org

Checks results and changes actions if needed: "successive approximation"

©2014 Waters

Considers how mental models affect current reality and the future

©2014 Waters Foundation, www.water

Considers short-term, long-term and unintended consequences of actions

BANK

Donut Shop

ing in Schools

Makes meaningful connections within and between systems

©2014 Waters Foundation, System
www.watersfound

Uses understanding of system structure to identify possible leverage actions

©2014 Waters Four

Recognizes the impact of time delays when exploring cause and effect relationships

©2014 Waters Foundation, Systems Thinking in Schools
www.watersfoundation.org

Recognizes that a system's structure generates its behavior

©2014 Waters Foundation, Systems
www.watersfoundation.org

Pays attention to accumulations and their rates of change

©2014 Waters Foundation, Systems Thinking in Schools
www.watersfoundation.org

Table of Contents

Foreword

By James Waters, Founder and Former CEO of Waters Corporation and Founder of the Waters Foundation

When I reflect on my career and life, one thing is certain: I have always been a systems thinker.

The fundamentals of systems thinking came naturally to me. As a young man growing up in Lincoln, Nebraska, there were many systems in place crucial to my productivity. The company that I grew from five employees has grown to over 6,000 today. It has seen lasting success because of the principles of systems thinking. For over 50 years, Waters Corporation has delivered innovative analytical laboratory instruments and software in over 100 countries.

In fact, I credit my success and dynamic perspective of the world to my ability to create a plan, identify challenges, implement changes and most importantly, harness a drive to deliver beneficial results. In short, I have built my life around always trying to do the right thing and "**deliver benefits.**"

It was not until the early 1980s, however, that I came to understand that this type of thinking had a name. Its creator, Dr. Jay Forrester of the Massachusetts Institute of Technology (MIT), introduced me to system dynamics. A few years later, I learned that Dr. Gordon Brown, Dean Emeritus of the College of Engineering at MIT, was bringing systems thinking into Tucson schools to enhance the way K-12 students approached learning. I jumped at the opportunity to get involved.

Since then, the Waters Foundation has implemented systems thinking in schools throughout the U.S. and internationally. We've trained more than 10,000 educators in the last 25 years. The value of systems thinking goes beyond the classroom — it is applicable to the boardroom, businesses, communities, relationships, and for virtually every person from every walk of life. It has been a great pleasure to see lives changed and minds broadened because of our work to share this process with others.

Our goal is simple: to make the world a better place. This goal may sound lofty, but that is the power of systems thinking — anything is possible with the right set of tools. That is why I am so proud to introduce this guidebook, which provides an in-depth explanation of the Habits of a Systems Thinker. I sincerely hope you find the tools as beneficial as I and countless others have over many years.

The authors of this book, **Tracy Benson** and **Sheri Marlin**, along with its many contributors, have done an outstanding job. You will be provided with real-life examples of the Habits and exercises to get you thinking about how you can apply the Habits to your own life and work.

I encourage you to approach these activities with an open mind. Do not shy away from challenges or ideas that may not come to you intuitively.

Challenges are our allies. They indicate that you are working toward a goal. When we create ways to overcome these challenges, I believe our best qualities and strongest intellect are brought to the surface. **What's more, the pleasure of delivering benefits is wonderful!**

I hope you enjoy lasting success from your time spent learning and practicing the Habits of a Systems Thinker.

Now, let's get started …

Getting started

This guidebook is for anyone who wants to actively learn about and engage in the process of becoming a systems thinker. The Habits of a Systems Thinker and systems tools that connect to them help develop deep and practical understanding of the world. No matter what your experience is with systems thinking, whether you are a novice or a skilled practitioner, this guide offers a workable approach to your personal development.

Designed as a hands-on workbook, each chapter highlights one of 14 Habits of systems thinking. The Habits of systems thinking are the foundational building blocks that define and describe the practices of a systems thinker. Whether you read this book to develop your leadership capabilities, coaching or teaching expertise or your parenting skills, the intention is to provide a wide and relevant practice field. The Habits offer practical ways of thinking that inform action. They provide a framework to help you reflect on your strengths and identify areas of growth. On the inside back cover, you will find a set of Habits cards to use as you work through this guidebook.

The guidebook includes a chapter for each of the 14 Habits of a Systems Thinker:

- Makes meaningful connections within and between systems
- Seeks to understand the big picture
- Changes perspectives to increase understanding
- Considers how mental models affect current reality and the future
- Observes how elements within a system change over time, generating patterns and trends
- Surfaces and tests assumptions
- Considers short-term, long-term and unintended consequences of actions
- Recognizes that a system's structure generates its behavior
- Uses understanding of system structure to identify possible leverage actions
- Considers an issue fully and resists the urge to come to a quick conclusion
- Identifies the circular nature of complex cause and effect relationships
- Recognizes the impact of time delays when exploring cause and effect relationships
- Pays attention to accumulations and their rates of change
- Checks results and changes actions if needed: "successive approximation"

Throughout each of the 14 Habits chapters, you will be engaged in practices that help build your potential to positively shape the future.

Each Habit chapter contains

- Descriptions, stories and examples related to the 5 sample systems
- Opportunities to help you Practice the Habit include reflection questions and strategies to build your understanding and skill
- Systems thinking tools: behavior-over-time graphs, stock and flow maps, causal loops, ladders of inference, connection circles and icebergs that apply to specific Habits, along with practice exercises with the tools
- Connections to other Habits of a Systems Thinker because no one Habit exists in isolation

Habits in action: exercises for next steps

Following the 14 Habits chapters, the Habits in Action section offers a wide range of exercises to support ongoing learning and collaborative sharing. The hands-on exercises and facilitated activities can be applied to work settings or life outside of work. The exercises listed below include comprehensive directions, required materials and scripted debrief questions.

- Habits of a Systems Thinker Self-Assessment for Individuals
- Habits of a Systems Thinker Self-Assessment in a Group Setting
- Habits of Leaders We Know and Admire
- Habits of a Systems Thinker Team Reflection Matrix
- Pipes and Marbles

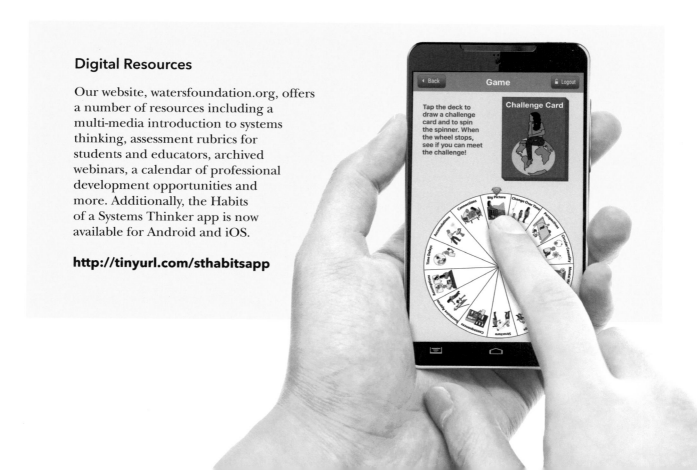

Digital Resources

Our website, watersfoundation.org, offers a number of resources including a multi-media introduction to systems thinking, assessment rubrics for students and educators, archived webinars, a calendar of professional development opportunities and more. Additionally, the Habits of a Systems Thinker app is now available for Android and iOS.

http://tinyurl.com/sthabitsapp

The Five Systems

Your understanding of the systems in your life and work will affect your decisions, your actions and the way you choose to live. We have identified five basic life systems that involve people. In this guidebook, each system is represented by a circular icon. These sample systems are included throughout the guidebook and are used in practice exercises and anecdotal examples. To get started, reflect on each of the five system types.

Icons	Sample Systems	Describe how each of these five systems relate to your life. How and why are they applicable and important to you?
	Well-being Personal well-being as a system involves your physical, emotional and social health. It also considers your state of being happy and prosperous.	_____ _____ _____ _____
	Family This system considers all of the people you choose to identify as your family, both immediate and extended, and may include people of all ages.	_____ _____ _____ _____
	Workplace Your workplace considers systems that could include paid employment, a volunteer position, your life's calling, or any role you play where you make a contribution to others.	_____ _____ _____ _____
	School As a place for learning and preparation, school is a system that is common to all of us. Your school could be a public, private, charter or home setting and could be a system that you attended or any other place of learning.	_____ _____ _____ _____
	Community Your community could be a place where you reside or a place where you belong. It could be a town, city, an affiliation or network. Your community involves relationships that are formed around a common purpose.	_____ _____ _____ _____

"For many years, I and others in my group at work have had The Waters Foundation's thirteen "Habits of a Systems Thinker" prominently posted on the walls by our desks. In the press of our day-to-day work, the "Habits" remind each of us of what it means to be a systems thinker, which each of us aspires to be. Now, it is so wonderful to have this new workbook that we can both learn from ourselves, and use to more effectively introduce the Habits to others, both at work, and in our relationships and connections beyond work. For me, a surprise in the book was inclusion of a fourteenth Habit not on our wall postings: "Makes meaningful connections within and between systems." This fourteenth Habit (1st in the book) led me to wonder about connections among the Habits. Then I noticed that many of the Habit chapters in the book contain sections titled, "Connection to other Habits of a Systems Thinker." Thank you, Tracy, Sheri and The Waters Foundation for the careful thought put into the book! I know, just as with your "Habits" wall postings, we will use your book over and over for many years to come…"

— Paul Newton, Systems Engineer in the Aerospace industry, Seattle, WA, USA

Benefits of a systems thinking approach

As you apply the 14 Habits of a Systems Thinker to the five systems in this guidebook, deepening your understanding and making connections, we believe the Habits will become valuable tools in your life and work. In our experience working with numerous organizations, we have found that the Habits are very effective in helping people achieve their desired results. The Habits offer both a common language and a shared framework for the kinds of thinking that produce meaningful change.

This book is also meant for sharing, so we encourage you to read and engage in the practice exercises with others. A systems thinking learning journey is collaborative and seldom a solo endeavor. Share this book with others, make it a focus with book study groups and use it to collaborate, share perspectives and develop the systems mindset that will optimize your ability to manage the complexity of today's world.

We hope you enjoy this guidebook and look forward to hearing about your experiences and applied learning.

Tracy Benson
President, Waters Foundation
t.benson@watersfoundation.org

Sheri Marlin
Chief Learning Officer, Waters Foundation
s.marlin@watersfoundation.org

Makes meaningful connections within and between systems

Just as puzzle enthusiasts find great satisfaction in pinpointing the correct spot for a complex puzzle piece, systems thinkers flourish when making connections within and between systems. It was a conscious decision to start with this Habit, in hopes that you will make your own meaningful connections as you work your way through this guidebook to the Habits of a Systems Thinker.

Making meaningful connections

Connections exist in nature, in learning and in relationships with others. The ability to make meaningful connections is a vital part of thinking and learning. Given the many contexts in which this Habit applies, it would be easy to trivialize the notion that everything is connected. A systems thinker continually makes meaningful connections and consciously weaves them together to produce clearer thinking and new ideas.

"In nature we never see anything isolated, but everything in connection with something else which is before it, beside it, under it and over it."

— Johann Wolfgang von Goethe, author

Natural world examples

Examples of connections exist throughout the natural world. A plant grows from a seed then flowers and produces fruit that eventually produces seeds. The plant is also connected to the birds and insects that pollinate its flowers. It needs sun, wind and water to grow. Predators or unfavorable weather can adversely affect it. The plant's survival is dependent on an intricate series of connections. On one hand, these connections happen naturally and without much thought or consideration, and yet the farmer, whose livelihood is dependent on producing a crop of fruit and having seeds for the future, has to give careful consideration to all of these factors.

A connection circle is a tool that helps you draw a picture of causal connections in a system. Let's think about the farmer and his crops.

Begin by placing some of the key parts of the system in a circle. A few have been provided to get you started, but feel free to add additional parts.

After you select key parts of your story, you are ready to make some connections. Here are some to get you started. The more plants there are, the more fruit is produced. The more fruit, the more seeds are available for future planting. The more predators (insects, deer, rabbits) there are, the fewer plants.

What additional connections can you add?

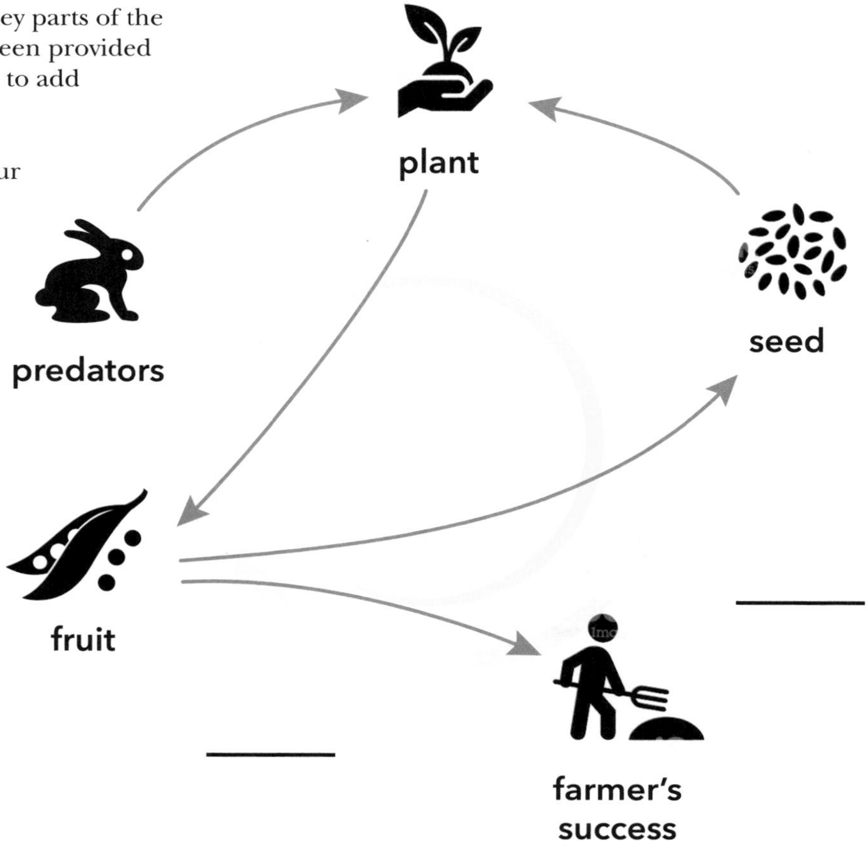

plant

seed

predators

fruit

farmer's success

As you draw the arrows, be sure to describe the connections you are making.

As a farmer cultivates crops, a systems thinker cultivates connections that promote learning. A growth mindset, the belief that intelligence is not purely innate, but can be developed through effort, can also be likened to planting the seeds of new knowledge into a fertilized mind ready to learn. Factors like curiosity, an inspiring teacher, or a good book serve as the sun, water and soil needed for growth and blossoming. A person's ability to learn new concepts or skills and to transfer that learning to new situations is critical for cultivating knowledge. Learning happens when connections are made within and between systems.

"Learning came alive for me and still does in those moments when I can see connections among different facts, findings or concepts."

— Ellen Gallinsky, *Mind in the Making[1]*

In order to see how connections are essential for learning, consider how humans develop language. From birth, children are able to produce a host of sounds, from very happy coos and sighs to urgent cries for help. As children develop, the sounds they make become more and more recognizable to people schooled in the native language. "Wah, wah" becomes understood as water. The request "wah, wah" is fulfilled with a verbal connection of, "Sure, you can have some water" and the young speaker begins to connect those sounds to a system for having his needs met. Eventually the word "water" is used in a sentence, resulting in an even more rapid exchange of need fulfillment. Language development continues to become increasingly sophisticated. The child eventually categorizes water as a drinkable liquid, but also recognizes that it is the substance that fills rivers and pools, and washes dirty hands. Further sophistication leads to an understanding that water can be a noun, but it can also be used as a verb when the child is asked to "water the plant." Over time this leads to an understanding of water issues such as drought, lack of access to clean drinking water or water rights contested by farmers and housing developers. This increased sophistication with language all comes from a series of connections and experiences.

Reflection: Describe a time when learning came alive for you because of connections you were able to make.

Systems thinkers further their learning by applying their understanding of systems to multiple contexts. A piano student may start his training with a rigorous regimen of practicing scales and drills, but to derive satisfaction from his new learning, the aspiring musician must transfer those skills to playing music. Once he is comfortable with the basics of one instrument he can use those foundational skills to quickly take on another instrument.

This type of connection, one that produces transfer, like from scales to music, can also take place between systems. A systems thinker looks to make connections between seemingly disparate systems. For instance, supply and demand of a popular product may follow the same oscillating pattern as the population of a species in a predator-prey relationship. The next exercise gives you the opportunity to practice making this type of connection, looking for patterns and similarities between two very different systems.

Applying new learning

A sophisticated application of this Habit is the ability to take in large amounts of information and make meaningful connections in order to produce insight and understanding into your system of interest.

Kim, the manager of a large accounting firm, is sent to a national conference. She spends five days learning from some great thinkers in her field about best practices in accounting and principles of leadership to help her become a more effective manager. The desired result is not just that Kim acquires the information, but also that she is able to apply the new learning to her current work situation. When Kim returns to work, she makes the connections between the conference and her work environment in order to adapt the learning to her firm's culture and translate her learning into actions that improve her performance and that of her team.

"Many believe effective networking is done face-to-face, building a rapport with someone by looking at them in the eye, leading to a solid connection and foundational trust." — Raymond Arroyo, journalist

Practice the Habit

One way to make connections is to find similarities in patterns, trends and structures.

How is the spread of a rumor similar to the spread of disease, as in an epidemic?

_____

_____

_____

_____

_____

How are the ups and downs of mood swings similar to the rise and fall of the stock market?

_____

_____

_____

_____

_____

Increasing happiness

In addition to the connections found in nature and in learning, some of the most profound connections we make are those connections that affect our relationships.

This Emotional Life, a three-part series on PBS, asserts, "Connecting with others is the single most important thing we can do for our own happiness." It goes on to say that when we are with other people, we are happier. When we are happier, we have better relationships, increasing the time we choose to spend with other people. Researchers have found that people are happier when they are with another person than when they are alone. The positive boost that comes from connecting is the same for both introverts and extroverts. There is evidence to suggest that human connections are essential for positive well-being.[2] The capacity to make connections is deeply ingrained in humans. Systems thinkers apply that natural inclination to understand human systems.

So regardless of the system being addressed, the ability to make connections and transfer information enhances our understanding of systems, our ability to learn and our capacity to work within a given system. Recognizing and acting on our innate need for human connections can lead to greater happiness and personal fulfillment.

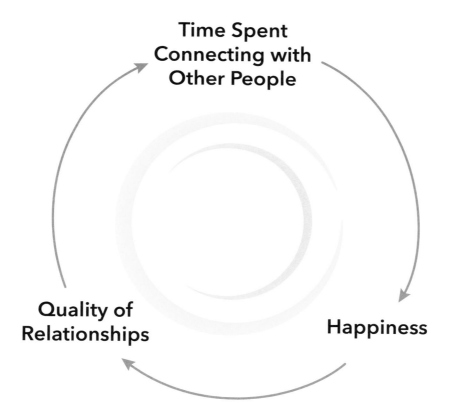

Reflection: Pause to think about the human connections that are important in your life.

The relationship loop is an example of a complex cause and effect relationship. Time spent with someone increases positive emotions, boosting happiness, thus improving relationships, which in turn makes you want to invest more time in the relationship. Seeds that grow into plants, which produce fruit to make more seeds, is another example of this Habit. Identifying cause and effect relationships is one way to make connections.

Reflection: The following questions may be useful in making meaningful connections within and between systems:

- Why would seeing connections be important in a system?

- How do connections affect understanding of the whole system?

- How does understanding of one system transfer to understanding of another system?

- How can different perspectives of a system bring value to the system?

- How does what you are learning connect to what you already know? How does integrating your new knowledge with your prior knowledge impact your understanding?

- What connections are you actively cultivating to increase your knowledge, your relationships and your overall well-being?

WHAT'S NEXT?

Now that you have examined some connections within your specific system of interest, ask yourself how those connections might give you a bigger picture of the current situation. Then proceed to the next chapter to learn how and why a systems thinker seeks to understand the big picture....

Practice the Habit

System definition: A system has two or more elements that interact to make a whole. Systems are everywhere. Some examples include cells, families, schools and office teams.

Identify a system of interest to you.

_____

List the parts of that system. Be as specific as you can.

_____

_____

What is the purpose or goal of your system of interest?

_____

How do things change over time in the system?

_____

_____

Build a connection circle, like the one about the farmer and his plants. Use arrows to show how the parts of your system connect.

What other systems are similar? How are they similar?

_____

_____

What new insights did you gain about your system of interest?

_____

_____

_____

Seeks to understand the big picture

Few experiences are more breathtaking than when standing on a balcony taking in the big picture view of a beautiful landscape. Depending on the time of day, patterns and colors vary as the sunlight casts shadows and brings depth to various elevations. When appreciating this sprawling view of the world, the various parts blend together as the colors of a sunset stand out and a bird takes flight from a faraway tree. Sometimes referred to as a 10,000 meter view, this vantage point can build new perspectives and greater understanding of a system. Systems thinkers intentionally seek this big picture orientation and are able to balance that view with timely attention to details when needed.

Spectator view

Have you ever watched a marching band perform during halftime of a sporting event or the opening ceremony of the Olympics? The goal of the performing group is to play music and create patterns that spell out words and formations that only spectators can appreciate. Each performer plays an important role as the formation moves and changes to create entertaining images.

The spectators in the stands have a big picture view of the performers on the field as their movements create geometric formations and artistic designs. The success of the performance is based on the individual paths of each performer and the interrelationships between the performing members. Are they lined up properly? Is the spacing equally divided? If one person falls out of step or fails to properly line up, the spectator's attention can quickly move to the part of the group that is not aligned.

Spectators with a big picture view easily notice slight irregularities, such as when performers are not quite in line or in step with their group.

Band members on the field have a very different view while performing. While marching, musicians pay attention to surrounding members, the markings on the field and the conductor. They do not have the advantage of seeing firsthand the big picture they make by working together because they have to pay attention to the details of their surroundings. They have to imagine the formations they create that are best appreciated by a broader perspective.

The same holds true when appreciating an orchestra or choral performance. Audience members listen to the blend of each instrumental section simultaneously playing their parts to produce the musical piece. At times, some instruments or solo voices are featured, but the beauty of the whole provides a synthesis of a musical system working together as one.

Restaurant review

Michael, a restaurant owner, read a negative online review of a customer's dining experience. This disappointing message expressed concern over one of his servers. The message motivated him to seek out more details about the situation. In addition to sharing the complaint with his employee, he considered, "Was this complaint a one time occurrence or more of a pattern?" If this mishap was one unfortunate incident, then the resulting actions would be quite different than if it had been recurring. Afterall, this server had worked in the restaurant for over three months, which was certainly long enough to assess competence. Michael felt he needed to seek the bigger picture based on the complaint. Resisting the urge to jump to a quick conclusion and identifying patterns and trends are complementary practices that help systems thinkers seek the big picture.

WORKPLACE EXAMPLE

American biologist and President of the Institute for Systems Biology, Leroy Hood, states, "If you just focus on the smallest details, you never get the big picture right."

Michael could have easily chastised his employee based on one negative review, but in order to "get it right," he gathered more information beyond this small detail.

Paying attention to the big picture may also involve attention to a collection of details.

"We often put so much energy into the big picture, we forget the pixels."

— Silvia Cartwright, former New Zealand Governor-General

The masterful teacher

Students were overheard talking about their teacher, "She must have eyes in the back of her head!" No matter what they did, even when she appeared to be looking the other way, their teacher always knew what was going on. Ms. Sampson observed everything — she noticed every detail of each and every interaction, no matter the energy level of her students. At the same time, she was able to maintain a clear picture of the goings on of the entire classroom and the degree to which children were behaving appropriately while they were engaged in learning. While working individually with Samantha, Ms. Sampson would notice and redirect a group of children who were admiring a new soccer ball that one student brought in for recess. She never missed anything that went on in her classroom. Ms. Sampson was able to maintain the balance between the detail of providing for individual students and the big picture of whole class engagement. This balancing act is a practiced skill that can increase understanding and influence in situations like busy classrooms. Teachers like Ms. Sampson are masterful in seeking to understand the big picture.

Balancing the big picture and the pixels is a practiced skill of many masterful teachers, like Ms. Sampson.

Systems thinkers balance the big picture view with attention to detail. Much like the focus on the forest while appreciating each tree, systems thinkers hold both views.

Systems thinkers can maintain the big picture that includes the 10,000-meter view while also giving attention to detail.

Practice the Habit

Systems thinkers take time and make efforts to capture a big picture view. It might mean scheduling some time away from the chaos of a busy office or active family and asking yourself a series of reflection questions.

How can I see beyond my day-to-day interactions and actions?

_____

_____

_____

How can I position myself to notice things I typically do not see?

_____

_____

_____

How can I increase the boundaries of my system to see a larger whole? The boundaries could be about a system's size (e.g. my assigned department versus my school, company or region). Or, could boundaries be about time (my view of this year versus my view of the next five years)?

_____

_____

_____

_____

_____

_____

How is my system of interest nested in a larger context? Can I see the effects of the larger system on smaller subsystems? (e.g. Is my child's grumpy behavior at home a condition of what has been going on with other children in the neighborhood or something else?)

_____

_____

_____

_____

_____

_____

Practice the Habit

1. How do I balance the value of seeking the big picture and honoring the importance of details?

   _____

   _____

   _____

   _____

   _____

   _____

2. How does this broader view provide you with a perspective that modified your view or enabled you to see something differently?

   _____

   _____

   _____

   _____

   _____

3. To what extent is your broader view on areas of influence, rather than on areas of concern that you cannot influence?

   _____

   _____

   _____

   _____

   _____

"Begin challenging your own assumptions. Your assumptions are your windows on the world. Scrub them off every once in a while, or the light won't come in." — Alan Alda, actor

In addition to Alda's recommendation, how can you increase the size of the window from which you view the world? Check in with others for opinions, views and insights. The check-ins will deepen your understanding of a bigger whole.

One way to seek the bigger picture is to look outside of one's own perspectives and seek the perspectives of others to help generate a new view. Efforts to check in with others and inquire about how they are viewing a situation or issue can increase your understanding as you learn more about the perspectives of others.

WHAT'S NEXT?

The next chapter will help you delve into the importance of changing perspectives to increase understanding and seeing the world from multiple points of view. Systems thinkers pause and suspend judgement when considering a new situation. They actively seek additional information. New, alternative perspectives often are a source of that additional information.

Changes perspectives to increase understanding

It's a bird. It's a tree. Or is it something else? What do you think is lurking behind the wall in this Habit image? No one really knows for sure, but this boy tries changing his perspective in order to increase his understanding of what might be behind the wall.

Consistently and intentionally seeking other perspectives is a hallmark of a successful systems thinker.

"If there is any one secret of success, it lies in the ability to get the other person's point of view and see things from his angle as well as your own." — Henry Ford, industrialist

The True Story of the Three Little Pigs, Told by A. Wolf[1], is a retelling of the familiar story "The Three Little Pigs," told from the perspective of a wolf. In this adapted story, the wolf explains that he really isn't big and bad. He was merely a neighbor to the pigs who wanted to borrow a cup of sugar. He knocked on the door of the first little pig's house and due to the pig's failure to use adequate construction, the house fell down, accidently killing the pig. It would have been wasteful of the wolf not to consume the meat. He goes on to explain what happened to each of the remaining pigs. A very different story than the one we typically remember, but a thought-provoking example of what it means to fully examine a situation from a different perspective.

Literature often helps us see things from different perspectives; such is the case when famous literary character Atticus Finch, in *To Kill a Mockingbird*, speaks specifically about the importance of considering the perspective of another. "'First of all,' he said, 'if you can learn a simple trick, Scout, you'll get along a lot better with all kinds of folks. You never really understand a person until you consider things from his point of view...until you climb into his skin and walk around in it.'"[2] Empathic thinking requires a form of perspective taking that is both circular and causal. It can be described as, "I understand you and try to feel what you feel; you then feel cared for and return the same sense of support to me."

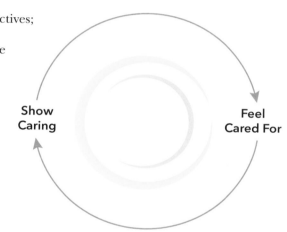

Show Caring

Feel Cared For

Perspective taking

Ellen Gallinsky's book *Mind in the Making* identifies seven life skills that promote learning and achievement in young children.[3] Perspective taking is one of those life skills. For children to be successful, they have to mature beyond a purely myopic view of the world and be able to take into consideration the needs and desires of others. A two-year-old grabbing a toy from his friend is a common scenario that creates a learning opportunity for the child. When an appropriate behavior (in this example sharing the toy) is modeled and reinforced, the child is able to practice a desired behavior, grow socially and emotionally and mature into an individual who gets along well with others.

Jen is a preschool teacher who recognizes that a two-year-old's tendency to grab a toy away from a playmate is a common behavior at this stage of development. She also understands that to help him mature beyond this developmental stage, she must intervene by modeling and reinforcing the appropriate behavior — sharing the toy. Giving her student the opportunity to learn how to take the perspective of another person allows him to grow socially and mature into an individual who gets along well with others. This scenario offers a very early example of what it means to change one's perspective in order to increase understanding.

Changing your perspective remains an important skill well into adulthood. It is essential to see the big picture of any system. In addition to considering the feelings, points of view and concerns of other people, it may also require that you suspend judgment in order to have a more complete picture of a particular situation.

After making an offer on a new home, Elena and Tom's realtor recommends an independent home inspection in order to protect their interest in their purchase. A few days after the inspection is completed, a report is sent to both the buyer and the seller. As buyers, Elena and Tom have vastly different perspectives on the content of the report than the sellers. When presented with a lengthy list of repairs, Tom and Elena expect that the seller will assume responsibility to repair each one, even down to the broken light switch cover. The seller receives the same report, and since there are no major issues or structural concerns, he is confident that the work he put in to prepare the house for sale is sufficient. He expects that Tom and Elena will be delighted at the worthy investment they are about to make in a home. These varying perspectives could result in loss of a sale if both the buyer and the seller are unwilling to suspend their own ideas about what constitutes a home in good condition and what the responsibility is of each party in the sale. Since Tom and Elena are committed to trying to see the report through the eyes of the seller, while keeping in mind what is important to them, they are able to come to a successful resolution. In order to practice changing perspectives, the buyer and the seller must be honest about their own perspective, suspend judgment and consider multiple perspectives in order to arrive at a reasonable conclusion about what repairs are truly necessary for both a successful sale and a responsible purchase.

Practice the Habit

Consider a familiar children's story or fable, other than *The Three Little Pigs*. What if you retold that story from a different perspective? How might the story be different? Take a minute to jot down some thoughts.

What story did you choose?

_____

What insights did you glean?

_____

_____

_____

_____

Practice the Habit

Have you ever gone to a movie with a close friend or family member and come out of the theater with a totally different viewpoint about the film? What was different in your perspectives on the film? How did what you each chose to pay attention to contribute to your different feelings about the movie?

_____

_____

_____

_____

_____

_____

_____

_____

_____

_____

Think about another example of a time you shared an experience with someone, but you had a very different perspective on the experience than the other person. How did your varying viewpoints affect your understanding of the experience?

_____

_____

_____

_____

_____

_____

_____

_____

_____

_____

The Sufi tale of "Elephant and the Blind Men"[4] also illustrates the importance of multiple perspectives. In this folktale, the blind villagers encounter an elephant and seek to determine what it is from their individual, singular vantage points. The one who touches the ear thinks the elephant to be a large fan. Feeling the trunk, another villager describes a hollow pipe that is both powerful and destructive. The legs seem to be pillars providing great support. All the individual perspectives are incorrect. It is only when combining all the diverse perspectives that the villagers can hope to determine the true nature of the elephant.

Reflection: Do I actively seek other perspectives, especially those with which I may disagree? Am I open to other points of view?

CONNECTION TO OTHER HABITS OF A SYSTEMS THINKER

A systems thinker surfaces and tests assumptions

One way to change your perspective to increase your understanding is by using the ladder of inference. The ladder of inference will be introduced in greater detail in chapter 6: *A systems thinker surfaces and test assumptions.*

The ladder of inference clarifies how our actions are driven by our beliefs, and our beliefs come from what we choose to pay attention to. We choose to pay attention to certain things because of our experiences. In order to change our perspective, we sometimes have to make a conscious decision to notice additional information. This often includes eliciting the experiences and perspectives of others. In doing so, we are able to increase our understanding of the system, which informs our beliefs and influences our actions.

WHAT'S NEXT?

In the next chapter you will learn that a systems thinker considers how mental models affect current reality and the future. An individual's personal perspective is strongly influenced by his mental models.

Additional examples of changing perspectives can be found in the mental model chapter. Here is one such example that encompasses both Habits. A group of friends are planning a vacation; they need to take multiple points of view into account in order for everyone to achieve what they want. Will they fly or drive? Spend one or two days at the beach? Each person's mental models about the trip, when shared openly, can affect the vacation planning and ultimately the success of the trip.

Practice the Habit

Identify a situation where you might be able to gain some clarity by changing your perspective. Apply the following questions to the situation to help you in seeking additional perspectives.

1. How does my point of view influence my understanding of the situation?

   _____

   _____

   _____

2. How might a different point of view inform my understanding of the situation?

   _____

   _____

   _____

3. Who could I approach to help me gain new perspectives on the situation?

   _____

   _____

   _____

4. If I truly understood that other person's perspective, what would I notice about my current situation?

   _____

   _____

   _____

5. How do different points of view influence my understanding of the system?

   _____

   _____

   _____

   _____

Considers how mental models affect current reality and the future

For those who live in places that see snow, it is easy to imagine two people having very different reactions to a new snowstorm. Based on experience, one might see it as an opportunity for play, while another sees snow as work because of added shoveling chores. Mental models are the assumptions and beliefs people develop over time from their experiences. Mental models influence the ways we interpret the world we experience. Because every individual has their own personally developed mental models based on their culture and life experiences, they oftentimes see the world in quite different ways.

> "Remember, always, that everything you know, and everything everyone knows, is only a model. Get your model out there where it can be viewed. Invite others to challenge your assumptions and add their own… Expose your mental models to the light of day."

— Donella H. Meadows, author of *Thinking in Systems: A Primer*

The staff meeting

The office manager, Judy, facilitated a staff meeting where she had to review new procedures for requesting and documenting vacation time. After the meeting, three different conversations took place:

CONVERSATION #1: JUDY AND MARCUS

Judy shared with Marcus, "I was a little nervous at first, but after I introduced the new process for submitting vacation leave, everyone seemed to really buy in. No one even asked a question. It went much better than I expected." Marcus responded, "I agree that people were quiet, but what made you think they were OK with what you said? Even though people were quiet, I sensed some tension and resistance."

CONVERSATION #2: ROBERTO AND ELSA

At the same time, in an office down the hall, Roberto said, "I can't believe we have to go through so much paperwork just to take a day off! Judy's expectations are unreasonable." Elsa then said, "If you felt that way, why didn't you say something? I don't really care about new procedures. I will just call in sick when I want to take a vacation day — so much easier!"

CONVERSATION #3: CHRIS AND MONICA

In another office, Chris debriefed the meeting with Monica. "I'm surprised that Judy and the other managers didn't ask for our input before dictating the new procedures." Monica responded, "I saw it a little differently. I don't have the time to give input about mundane things like paperwork related to vacation leave. I'm glad they made a decision and just told us what to do!"

When people look at, listen to and experience the very same situation, they can leave with diverse impressions about what occurred. Whether people are reading the same book or attending the same event, individuals derive their opinions and impressions based on their preferences and what they choose to pay attention to and value.

People pay attention to different things and notice aspects of their experience based on what is important to them. For example, a past experience, family value or a personal priority can influence what people hold as most significant. Important priorities and values contribute to the development of mental models.

Mental models are sometimes referred to as paradigms. In Donella Meadows' primer, *Thinking in Systems,* she discusses key places to intervene in a system to get more of what you want. These interventions are called leverage points. She proposes that one of the highest, most impactful places to intervene in a system is with the paradigms or mental models people hold of the system. She writes, "You can say paradigms are harder to change than anything else about a system…there's nothing physical or expensive or even slow in the process of paradigm change. In a single individual it can happen in a millisecond. All it takes is a click in the mind, a falling of scales from the eyes, a new way of seeing. Whole societies are another matter—they resist challenge to their paradigms harder than they resist anything else." (pp. 163-64)

CONNECTION TO OTHER HABITS OF A SYSTEMS THINKER

Uses understanding of system structure to identify possible leverage actions

As Meadows suggests, systems thinkers actively work to understand the mental models that exist in the system. Mental models affect what goes on in human systems. Oftentimes, leverage is most effective when those in the system are willing to be flexible, shift or even let go of their existing mental models and become open to new views and possibilities.

Mental models, in the form of paradigms, can be difficult to change. It is unwise to think you can single-handedly change or shift another person's mental model. However, individuals can develop and nurture the environmental conditions where people can reflect and consider their own mental models. This safe culture of reflection can foster desirable shifts and paradigm adjustments. It is a personal choice to be open to the "click in the mind" that opens up new possibilities. Systems thinkers recognize the power and influence of mental models, and this important Habit of thinking reminds us that mental models are people's current reality and greatly influence their view of the future. In addition, Meadows goes deeper into her analysis of places to intervene in systems, and encourages us all to free ourselves of the strong influence of our paradigms or mental models.

"That is to keep oneself unattached in the arena of paradigms, to stay flexible, to realize that no paradigm is 'true,' that every one, including the one that sweetly shapes your own worldview, is a tremendously limited understanding of an immense and amazing universe that is far beyond human comprehension." — Donella Meadows

This flexibility of thinking and interpreting reminds us to enter each situation with a beginner's mind in order to take in a wide pool of information. There is value in staying mindful of how our mental models are developed and how they influence our decision-making and actions.

Practice the Habit

Think of a time when you shared your mental model about something you care about.
What did you learn about yourself when you shared it?

_____

_____

How can you invite others to share their mental models?

_____

_____

How do you respond when mental models differ?

_____

_____

Think about the last meeting you attended or facilitated. It could be a work-related meeting or a community-based gathering. What was your impression of the meeting?

_____

_____

How did people hear and interpret what was being said?

_____

_____

How did the facilitator provide participants opportunities to voice their interpretations?

_____

_____

How might you interpret silence?

_____

_____

The systems thinking iceberg: mental models as the foundation

The systems thinking iceberg is a framework that applies many of the systems thinking Habits to the understanding of complex systems. Each level calls for a specific way of thinking about a system of interest.

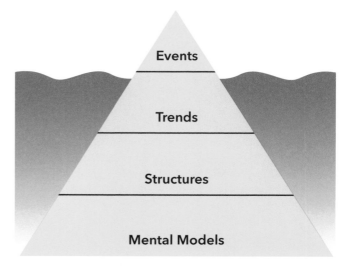

This framework helps deepen the understanding of complex systems. The tip of the iceberg, the only visible piece above the water level, involves the day-to-day events and occurrences that you experience. This common, but limited view produces a surface understanding of what a system is about. For example, a store manager can greet customers, observe how employees are serving those customers and assess inventory by looking at shelves and storage rooms.

From these day-to-day events, she can get some sense of whether or not the business is thriving.

Good managers are systems thinkers. They intentionally go below the surface of the waterline of the iceberg and view their business systems at a variety of levels. Each level of the iceberg below the water line connects with specific Habits of a Systems Thinker.

Trends

Trends focus on the dynamics of a system. What are the essential elements that are changing over time? How are elements changing and what is causing those shifts? This level of the iceberg connects to the Habit, *observes how elements within systems change over time generating patterns and trends* (see chapter 5 for a more detailed description and additional practice exercises). Obvious trends for a store manager include sales, total revenue, inventory and outcomes from price reductions. Broadening the boundary of what could be important when focusing on essential elements that change over time might be market research, customer needs, local conditions and competitor activity. In addition, trends in employee satisfaction, skill development, employee turnover and promotion opportunities are also important to a successful business.

Structure

Systems thinkers pay attention to what is causing the shape of trend lines. For our store manager, one obvious structure is the relationship between supply and demand. It is at this level that systems thinkers fully examine the design of their system and how one aspect affects another, which in turn influences others. When supply is high and demand is low, it is time to hold a sale and cut prices. On the other hand, when demand is high for a popular product, it is important to make efforts to order and stock that product in order to maintain customer satisfaction and revenue.

The structure level helps show how important system elements (like inventory, customer demand, pricing and customer satisfaction) are interdependent. And the interdependent structures influence the previously identified patterns and trends. The Habit of a Systems Thinker that connects to this level is, *recognizes that a system's structure generates its behavior* (see chapter 7).

This structural understanding can help individuals like our store manager trace a potential ripple effect when a small change or adjustment generates other changes in seemingly unexpected places. For example, our manager may want to give careful attention to competitors' efforts so that she can gain new insights and ideas that could positively influence the business. Encouraging positive relationships among the competition may seem counterintuitive to a business wanting to get ahead and beat out the competition, yet this relationship could provide strategies for initiating a positive ripple effect resulting in mutual benefits for all.

Mental models

Mental models are an essential aspect of a system's structure. Think about all of the stakeholders who contribute to and are affected by the system. When the various mental models from this diverse stakeholder pool are made explicit, a deeper understanding of how human elements contribute to the workings of the system become evident. It is difficult to fully understand a system without an appreciation of the different mental models of all involved. Without consideration of mental models, changes in systems structures (e.g. policies, laws, procedures) will only result in surface modifications. In order for the small business manager to best address her challenges, she should carefully consider the mental models of her employees, her customers and her competition, in addition to giving conscious attention to the mental models she holds about the business. This human aspect of system structure is often considered the highest leverage area. When individuals embrace a mindset that is open, flexible and honest, a system will be adaptive and productive.

Shifting gears a bit, consider the tension that exists globally because of vastly different mental models around serious issues like gun control, immigration, social justice, healthcare and religious freedom. These issues inundate our news feeds and social media sources daily. News events draw our attention to the day-to-day event level of the iceberg. Policy makers react to these events and struggle to create structures to help alleviate the existing tension. They look for structures that will help change the course of events and adjust the system to more desirable trends. The iceberg helps us realize that in order to change undesirable patterns of system behavior (e.g. violence, hate, inequity and blame), it is essential to rise above one's own mental models and deepen the understanding of the system by considering a wide variety of mental models that drive how a system behaves. Isolated experiences, individual values, socio-economic position and culture are just some of the factors that influence the mental models that are formed across sectors. Without intentional efforts to surface and understand the mental models of diverse groups and individuals, a reliance on change in physical structure, like policies or laws, will only place a temporary band-aid on the symptoms of ongoing problems. In order to sustain lasting positive change in systems, a more fundamental approach centered on the mental model level of the iceberg is essential.

QUESTIONS TO ASK WHEN PRACTICING THIS HABIT:

How are current mental models helping achieve the system's desired outcomes of the system?

How are they hindering progress?

How am I helping others see the influence that mental models have on our decision-making?

Practice the Habit

Think about a significant event in your community, your state or country. Use the iceberg to help you surface the mental models that influenced the event. How did the event impact, modify or sustain existing mental models?

Sketch your ideas in the blank iceberg below.

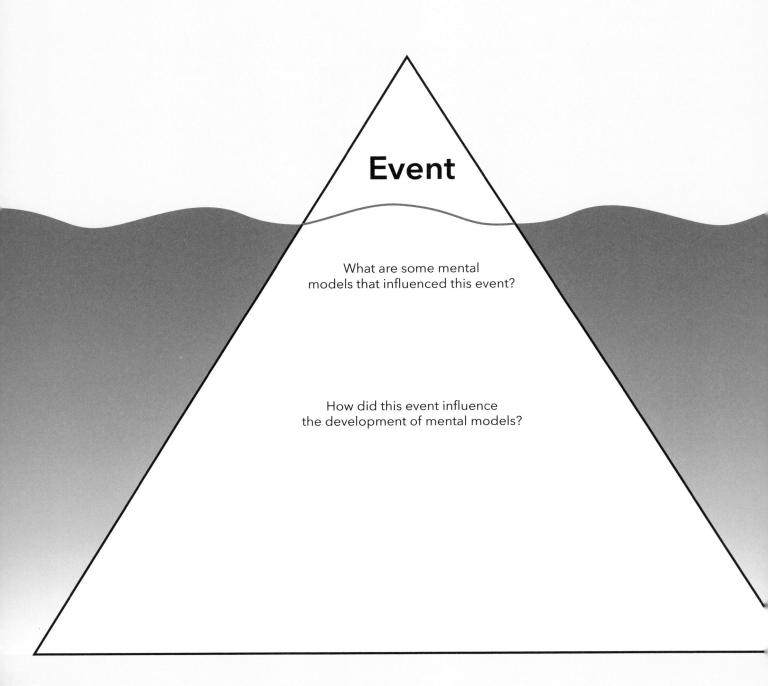

Event

What are some mental
models that influenced this event?

How did this event influence
the development of mental models?

"You can discover more about a person in an hour of play than in a year of conversation." — Plato, philosopher

Providing people a kinesthetic, playful experience can create a safety net for encouraging flexibility and the surfacing and examining of diverse mental models. Place small tubs of modeling clay or PlayDoh® on tables during a meeting or group conversation, so that people can feel the pliable nature of the clay as a reminder to remain flexible in their thoughts and opinions. To help debrief this experience, note how difficult the clay is to mold once it is dried up. The importance of constant molding and manipulation of the clay is the same process that encourages mental model shifts and the development of new insights. Suggest that people share one another's clay and combine colors and forms. This too can serve as a powerful metaphor for collaborative thinking that is malleable and flexible.

CONNECTION TO OTHER HABITS OF A SYSTEMS THINKER

Makes meaningful connections within and between systems

When people are asked to make a connection between an experience and a concept like the use of modeling clay and examination of mental models, they are practicing the Habit, *makes meaningful connection within and between systems*. Metaphorical experiences help people make new neural connections between seemingly disparate occurrences.

Surfaces and tests assumptions

In addition, the above exercise with clay can encourage the practice of a related Habit, *surfaces and tests assumptions*. If your clay represents your assumptions, you can share it, describe its color and shape and connect the physical representation by also describing your opinion. When your opinion or assumption becomes visible for all to see and understand, it is vulnerable to questioning and testing. Your opinions and assumptions are aspects of your mental models.

WHAT'S NEXT?

The next chapter will introduce you to a tool that helps make thinking visible through the use of a simple graph that shows change. Read on to learn about strategies to explore the essential systems concept of change over time.

Observes how elements within systems change over time, generating patterns and trends

Change is an inherent property of systems. A person can change a shirt or change her mind in a moment's notice, but unlike a one-time-event view of change, systems thinkers focus on the nature of change over time.

Measuring change

The ability to observe how elements within systems change over time, and the means to represent that change, are important practices of a systems thinker. Change can be measured in concrete ways as with the changing height and weight of a growing child. But change can also be documented from a particular point of view, as in the changing temperament or level of independence of a developing child. For example, a parent may view her teenage daughter's repeated efforts to become more independent as growing rebellious behavior, whereas the daughter views her independence as a part of growing up. For the daughter, becoming more mature means being less dependent on her parents.

"To exist is to change, to change is to mature; to mature is to go on creating oneself endlessly." — Henri Bergson, philospher

The ability to observe change and make those observations visible helps people communicate viewpoints about how and why things change. Like the spread of a tweet or instagram post or the ups and downs of the stock market, trends are part of daily life and our changing world. We hear about them, see them illustrated in newspapers and feel them personally. Observing changing elements in a system as patterns and trends can be practiced in all kinds of systems. Systems thinkers come to do this naturally.

Examples include:

 WORKPLACE: morale of a company's employees

 FAMILY: stress that a family experiences as children grow up

 WELL-BEING: time spent reading for enjoyment

 SCHOOL: excitement when starting a new school year

 COMMUNITY: number of cars on a freeway throughout the day

Reflection: Think about something that has changed in your life and reflect on these questions:

- Is this a one-time occurrence, or has it happened before?

- If I have seen it happen before, can I name the key element that is changing and describe how it is changing?

- How fast or slow are things changing?

- How does the rate of change influence my next steps?

- Was the change a result of a new program, initiative or event? What will change look like in the future?

Making patterns and trends visible with behavior-over-time graphs

Behavior-over-time graphs (BOTGs) are simple tools that illustrate patterns and trends. Basically, a BOTG can show through a quick drawing of a graph how something changes over time. Time is always on the "x," or horizontal axis and the element that is changing is on the "y," or vertical axis. BOTGs can show trends using numerical data, for example when a child with diabetes keeps track of her changing blood sugar levels (see below).

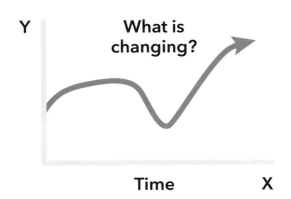

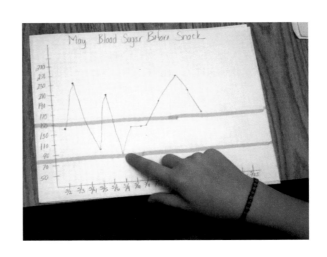

Quality of communication

Perceptual impressions of change also provide valuable information about the system. These examples show two views of the quality of communication for an organization's leadership team. Each leader's graph may appear slightly different, but the perception of the change tells a story of personal experience.

The stories of the graphs provide key indicators of what is generating the ups and downs of the trend lines. Efforts to make perceptual change visible is a good first step to sharing honest opinions about the current state of the system and clarifying the evidence that people attach to important variables like quality of communication.

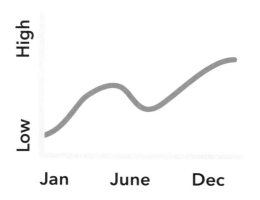

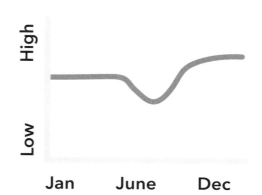

"My view of our communication is that it was poor at best at the start of the year. We improved a bit when we decided to meet once a week, but then around May and June, people got too busy and stopped showing up. We assumed that we all knew what each other was doing. These unchecked assumptions caused problems, and it was a good thing that Jack brought this up in late June. He helped us get on track and our communication continued to improve." — Elsa

"I thought we were communicating fairly well in the beginning of the year. People were responding to text messages and emails on a regular basis. I also saw a dip in June, but it was minor. June is just our busy month, so we should expect communication to suffer a bit. I'm sure Jack helped, but I think we just need to expect things to get a little crazy each June." — Marcus

When individuals in a group each graph their perceptions of how an essential system element has changed over time, each person can quickly observe the diversity of how various people see the system. Individuals each "tell the story" of his or her graph while providing narrative evidence. This process of drawing and explaining graphs from an individual point of view is a visual way to achieve changing perspectives to increase understanding. Revisit chapter 3, *Changing perspectives to increase understanding, to help connect these two Habits.*

In the case of trend lines that show numerical data or lines that show patterns informed by perception, one might ask when viewing a change over time, "Is the trend growing or declining, leveling off or oscillating?" The shape of the change becomes the story of the change. When individuals create BOTGs they not only visually describe the nature of the change, but they also document the rationale for the shape of the pattern or trend over time. For example, a story of a graph might go like this: "In the beginning, the line goes up because…and then levels off because…and eventually goes back down because…"

"Time is a dressmaker specializing in alterations." — Faith Baldwin, author

Current and future trends

BOTGs show how an element has changed in the past, but it can also show what a predicted change might look like. The Social Systems Lab at the Brown School of Social Work at Washington University has developed a process or script to help groups map and model systems of interest.[1] One of their scripts focuses on the use of BOTGs to show change over time in the past, and the hopes and fears about how that same element might change in the future. By incorporating the future into observations about patterns and trends of essential system elements, systems thinkers can together envision a wide range of anticipated results. When BOTGs are created by small groups of people, conversations that surface mental models about the past and future can move people to a fuller understanding of their system. This example tracks the number of clients a start-up company is developing over time. After "today" the blue line tracks the hope and the orange line tracks the fear. In this example, the graph helps surface and test people's assumptions about client growth. As people share their explanations for their predictions, the two future scenarios would include the factors that could cause both growth and decline.

Preschool trends

One of the most powerful examples of how BOTGs help people see and understand patterns and trends comes from a preschool class of four-year-olds. Mrs. Lee's class was reading a series of picture book stories and making simple graphs of changes over time in elements such as levels of happiness, the fear of the main characters, or

changes in the number of animals or amount of plants in a garden. After the teacher read each story aloud, the class would collectively draw a BOTG of the changes in the key element and then discussed the graph. The teacher would then hang the graph on a classroom wall. After a few weeks following this routine, a child looked at the series of graphs that had been drawn from different books and noticed that some of the trend lines were similar. She noticed several up-and-down lines showing that the level of change was sometimes going up and sometimes going down from several different stories. She proudly pointed out this similarity and named those stories that had up-and-down graphs "crown stories." The graphs looked like a queen's crown and that clever label helped categorize a pattern.

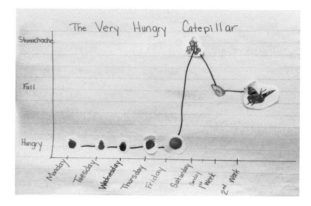

That young girl's revelation inspired the thinking of her classmates as they started naming other alike-looking graphs as "slides," "stairs," "tables" and "smiles." Now when listening to stories, the four-year-olds actively seek patterns and name them accordingly. Because the children have internalized the understanding that change can have shape and pattern, they use their own labels to identify the generic nature of patterns and trends they see and experience. Are we trending toward a generation of systems thinkers? Let's hope so!

Perceptual trends

Trends are effective ways to track progress in the workplace. Data-driven trends can show quarterly profits and losses, student achievement data, employee attendance, ratings of customer satisfaction and movement toward a goal (e.g. golf scores, pounds lost or steps walked each day). In addition to hard, numerical data, trends graphs can help make meaning of people's perceptions. Specific points on the graph at any point in time are not nearly as important as the shape of the line. Some BOTGs represent generic patterns. These generic patterns of change are actually "grown-up" versions of the same graphs that the young children creatively named.

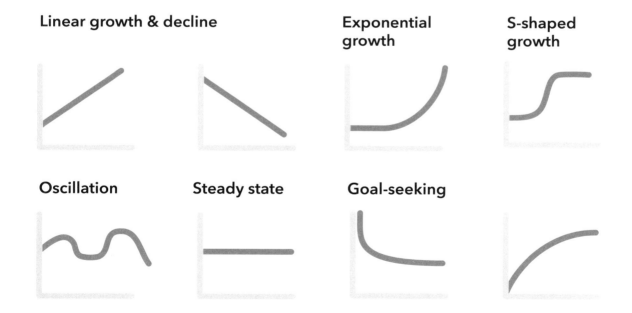

Linear growth & decline

Exponential growth

S-shaped growth

Oscillation

Steady state

Goal-seeking

Practice the Habit

Exercise #1: Choose one generic BOTG graph from the previous page (e.g. Linear growth or decline, oscillation, s-shaped growth, goal-seeking). Think of a scenario or story from your work or family setting that has a trend that matches the graph you chose. With another person, talk through your story while pointing at various parts of the graph, and see what kind of conversation develops.

Questions to think about:
Which graphs were easiest to apply to your workplace or family setting?

Which trends were more difficult to connect to your workplace or family setting?

Why?

Exercise #2: If you keep a journal, identify important trends in your life that you are trying to impact. In addition to words, draw a BOTG in your journal to track your progress and make the change visible. For example, "I am trying to not be so negative when I am in team meetings." Draw a BOTG as a part of your journal entry and use it to show how your level of negativity changes over a week's time. This is a very quick way to enter a reflection in your journal even if you do not have the time to write a meaningful entry. Use the graph to show the shape of change as influenced by causal factors.

Level of Negativity

High

Low

Mon   Tues   Wed   Thurs   Fri

Changing Element _____

High

Low

Mon   Tues   Wed   Thurs   Fri

"Progress is impossible without change, and those who cannot change their minds cannot change anything." — George Bernard Shaw, author

Practice the Habit

Reflect on these questions as you consider important trends that impact you, your work and life.

What trends are important for you to pay attention to as you strive to achieve goals or desired outcomes?

_____

_____

What types of trends do you tend to notice?

_____

_____

How might these tendencies create blind spots that limit your ability to recognize other important patterns and trends?

_____

_____

_____

How does your perspective influence the ways you see change? How can you become open to other perspectives that may help you see patterns in different ways?

_____

_____

_____

WHAT'S NEXT?

BOTGs provide individuals ways to make their assumptions about change visible to others. When people reveal the way they see how important aspects of a system change over time, they also can compare and contrast their assumptions with others. To test the assumptions, the story of graphs should include the causal evidence people connect to their trend lines. For example, the # of clients will go up if we increase our marketing efforts. Or, the # of clients may level off if we have saturated our limited market. The next chapter, _Surfaces and tests assumptions_ will help you further explore this Habit of a Systems Thinker.

Surfaces and tests assumptions

Sugar   Vitamins

Super Star Cereal

©2014 Waters Foundation, Systems Thinking in Schools
www.watersfoundation.org

Surfaces and tests assumptions

What makes Super Star Cereal super? The boy reads the label and sees a deliciously sweet cereal. The girl looks at the same cereal box and sees a nutrient-dense cereal that delivers a full day's worth of vitamins. Who has the more accurate picture? They won't really know until they take the time to surface their assumptions and to test each assumption with a careful analysis of the information.

Investigating beliefs

The systems thinker articulates his belief, in this case taste or nutrition, and then looks for evidence to support or refute his belief. Perhaps Super Star Cereal is able to deliver both great taste and great nutrition, but the two systems thinkers pictured here will only be able to make that determination after they have investigated their beliefs.

It takes courage to make your thinking visible to others. Whether you are stating an opinion on a community issue or sharing your personal impression of social media, surfacing the assumptions you hold can be risky. The risk involves the reaction of others who may hold a different belief about the same topic or experience.

Research provides an example of surfacing and testing assumptions. Testing assumptions is fundamental to the research process. Research begins with a hypothesis. From there an experimental design is developed, data are collected and analyzed, and then conclusions are drawn. As a specific example, there have been a number of studies that have investigated the benefits and trade-offs of having single-gender, or all-girl and all-boy, schools.[1] The studies are driven by the assumption that boys and girls may perform better in single-gender schools, as mixed-gender schools may offer an increase in distractions between boys and girls or influence the nature of participation in class. These specific assumptions inform the collection and review of statistical data.

The data from a single study can present one view. But what happens when conflicting studies and results both support and refute the hypothesis? A systems thinker takes on a wider view of analysis, increasing the likliehood that all assumptions and supporting data are surfaced, and makes efforts to test beyond single-sample studies or short-term investigations. Using research is one way to surface and test assumptions.

"The greatest compliment that was ever paid me was when one asked me what I thought, and attended to my answer. It takes two to speak the truth — one to speak and another to hear." — Henry David Thoreau, essayist

Reflection: Identify a current event that is being fueled by potentially erroneous assumptions.

How do you get in the habit of testing your own assumptions? By asking questions, seeking additional sources of information and reflecting more carefully on how you arrived at a particular conclusion.

The power of listening

The importance of listening also contributes to the power of this Habit of a Systems Thinker. When we listen only to our own inner voice, we become quickly wed to our own ideas and may not pause to consider additional information. Surfacing and testing assumptions goes two ways. The Habit is practiced not only by speaking and sharing our ideas with others, but by actively pursuing the thoughts, ideas and perspectives of others.

"It is the province of knowledge to speak. And it is the privilege of wisdom to listen." — Oliver Wendell Holmes, Supreme Court Justice

"I really like to surface my assumptions because I like telling people what I think. But I don't like testing them because sometimes when I test them, I discover I am wrong. I don't like being wrong." — Eighth grade student

Practice the Habit

Systems thinkers recognize that their assumptions may be wrong. Think about a time when you realized you were wrong. Describe that time and the new information that led you to correct your erroneous assumptions.

_____

_____

_____

_____

_____

_____

_____

_____

_____

_____

The ladder of inference

The ladder of inference, developed by Chris Argyris, Harvard professor of Education and Organizational Behavior, is a tool that can be helpful in practicing the Habit of *surfaces and tests assumptions*. The theory behind the ladder is that we all have experiences that lead us to pay attention to certain things. In turn, we add meaning to what we notice based on our personal and cultural background. It is from this filtered input that we develop our beliefs. The real power of this tool is in recognizing that our beliefs lead to our actions and what we choose to notice in the future. Unexamined, highly-filtered beliefs can lead to potentially embarrassing or even detrimental actions.

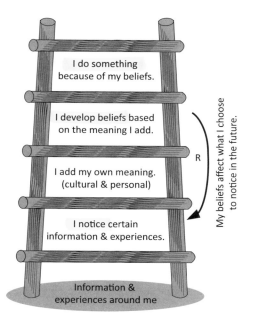

Surfacing assumptions with colleagues

Maria's team has regularly scheduled meetings at 1:00 p.m. every Wednesday. Maria notices that her co-worker Susan is frequently late for these weekly meetings. Maria works very hard to be on time and considers it a sign of disrespect when someone is late. She begins to notice other things Susan does that she finds impolite, such as checking her phone during meetings. On this particular Wednesday, Susan arrives at 1:10 p.m. and asks Maria to recap a critical piece of information that she missed due to her tardiness. Susan then offers a modification to the current course of action. Her suggestion causes Maria to reach her breaking point. She publicly discredits Susan's input, explaining that she is not a contributing member of the team and that she finds her behavior rude. At that point, another member of the team explains that Susan has actually been part of a weekly call to help out the district manager. She has not been willfully late and disrespectful, but rather has discreetly been handling a difficult client. In that moment, Maria realizes that she has jumped up the ladder of inference and allowed the high-value she places on promptness to cause her to misjudge a colleague. She went from observation (Susan is late), to belief (Susan is disrespectful), to action (publicly discrediting her contributions). Maria apologizes for her action and is eventually able to restore a trusting, collegial relationship with Susan.

One way we "jump up the ladder" and fail to adequately test our assumptions is in making judgments about people; hence the popular phrase, "You only have one chance to make a good first impression." No matter how open-minded or forward-thinking we believe ourselves to be, the reality is we are jumping to conclusions all the time.

CONNECTION TO OTHER HABITS OF A SYSTEMS THINKER

Considers how mental models affect current reality and the future

Once we come to believe our assumptions are true, they become our mental models. You may want to go back to chapter 4 and reference the mental model you reflected on in the final practice exercise. Now that you know a bit more about the ladder of inference, what new insights do you have about how you developed that belief? Practicing the Habit of considering our mental models will make us more aware of our own assumptions.

Reflection, inquiry and advocacy

Three practices that help you use the ladder of inference are reflection, inquiry and advocacy.

Reflection allows you to suspend judgment and become more aware of your own thinking. Reflection is a time to make sure that you are paying attention to all the relevant data related to your system of interest.

Inquiry encourages you to ask questions that help you understand someone else's thinking. When inquiring about someone's thinking, ask open-ended questions in order to seek clarification and help you better understand what others are noticing that leads them to the beliefs and actions they take.

Advocacy is a skill in which you make your own thinking and reasoning more visible to others by describing what influences your beliefs and actions.

CONNECTION TO OTHER HABITS OF A SYSTEMS THINKER

Observes how elements within systems change over time, generating patterns and trends

The previous chapter showed how graphs are used to help systems thinkers pay attention to changes in the system. The visual nature of a behavior-over-time graph makes the assumptions behind the graph explicit. We can disguise our thoughts in words, but the line on the graph tells a story that makes our thinking clear.

Practice the Habit

Think of recent situations in which you could have used reflection, inquiry and/or advocacy to surface and test your assumptions.

_____

_____

_____

_____

_____

_____

_____

Behavior-over-time graph

Another tool that is useful when surfacing and testing assumptions is a behavior-over-time graph (BOTG). BOTGs help us see changes in a system and raise awareness of how people see change in different ways. When groups of people are asked to graph the change they see in quality of communication or level of commitment for a particular project, BOTGs can help surface the different ways people perceive that change. For example, a work team is asked, "How have you seen our level of effectiveness change over the past six months as we worked together on this project?" After spending time individually reflecting and drawing graphs, individuals surface their own interpretation of the team's level of effectiveness. The graphs may look very different based on people's position, the role they play or the value they place on various aspects of effectiveness.

The graphs can show a wide range of diverse views, but the richness of the tool is that it gives people a visual way to surface their assumptions and test them by telling the story of their graphs. Let's listen in as this team shares the stories associated with their individual graphs.

Person A

"Six months ago, I remember us really struggling to work together because we all had different ideas about how we should approach this project. Once we had some time together and had a chance to hear one another out, it seemed that our effectiveness just shot up very quickly. I love working with all of you!"

Person B

"When we first got together, we were all so excited about the project that I felt our ability to work together grew fairly rapidly. Then, after some time, the project became frustrating and a little boring. I think we plateaued because we were ready to move on, yet I think we can get another upswing."

Person C

"Like Person B, I felt our initial enthusiasm actually had us working together really well right off the bat. After some time that effectiveness seemed steady. I think about three months ago we hit a point where we had trouble agreeing about next steps, and we took a dip when we couldn't agree about our roll out. I think we currently need to work on our collaboration — we are doing too many things independently and not working together, yet I, too enjoy working with this team even when times are tough!"

Person D

"In the beginning of our work together, I saw it kind of like Person A and B where we were excited about the possibilities and really were good at sharing ideas. At one point I thought I was part of a dream team the way we communicated and strategized about a workable plan. Then, when it came to deciding on one approach for implementation, our effectiveness broke down as we each tried hard to sell our specific idea versus efforts to compromise or reach a consensus. I think we are stuck."

All four of the above individuals participated in the same project, but each viewed the team's level of effectiveness very differently.

Practice the Habit

Consider a belief you have about your community. Remember in this book we have defined community as a place you reside or a place where you belong. It involves relationships formed around a common purpose. Perhaps your assumption is about a recent neighborhood association ruling, a decision by the board of your community group or your city's plan to decrease fees for using recreational facilities. Then use the questions to walk yourself up the ladder as a way to surface and test the assumptions contained in your belief.

COMMUNITY EXAMPLE

Questions for you to consider about yourself (walk yourself up the ladder and begin at #1):

5. How are your actions influenced by your beliefs?

_____

_____

4. How do your current beliefs influence what you notice?

_____

3. What in your personal background or experience influences your current viewpoint?

_____

2. What else could you choose to pay attention to that might enhance your understanding of your community?

_____

1. What are you noticing about the current state of your community?

_____

Based on this walk up the ladder, what evidence do you have that your assumptions are correct? Incorrect?

_____

_____

Consider your possible actions by asking yourself some "what if" questions. For example, "What if I stood up for my neighbor in opposition to the neighborhood association?" "What if I wrote a letter expressing support for the lower fees?"

_____

_____

Consider this…

How much more likely are people to hold differing views when they are looking at the same issue but are coming from a vastly different base of information and experience?

How can this exercise increase a team's understanding of their own work, their relationships and the roles they play?

Actively practicing this Habit helps everyone develop a more accurate understanding of the current situation.

Having groups draw BOTGs prior to discussing their perspectives can be very useful in helping groups surface and test their personal assumptions and exposing pervasive mental models (assumptions) within the group. The graphing exercise is excellent for individuals as well. Perhaps you want to test your assumptions about your current fitness practices. Graphing multiple variables, such as weight, cardio fitness, calorie intake and stamina will give you much more information than testing your assumptions against only one static measurement.

So whether you are contemplating which cereal to purchase or reflecting on your team's effectiveness, taking the time to surface and test your assumptions and evaluate your choices in light of all the available evidence is an important thing to do. Using tools like the ladder of inference and behavior-over-time graphs can help you actively practice this Habit.

Changes perspectives to increase understanding

©2014 Waters Foundation, Systems Thinking in Schools
www.watersfoundation.org

CONNECTION TO OTHER HABITS OF A SYSTEMS THINKER

Changes perspectives to increase understanding

Regularly practicing the Habit of surfacing and testing assumptions will naturally lead to taking into account the perspectives of others. Reflecting on the basis of your own assumptions leads to inquiring about the root cause of the beliefs of others as well.

WHAT'S NEXT?

Equipped with a solid understanding of how our experiences form our beliefs and the importance of surfacing and testing your beliefs, you are now ready to use that information to take a close look at the structure of a system. In the next chapter, you will learn that system structures are all around us and have a significant impact on how systems behave.

Recognizes that a system's structure generates its behavior

©2014 Waters Foundation, Systems Thinking in Schools
www.watersfoundation.org

Recognizes that a system's structure generates its behavior

The wind lifts the kite higher in the air as the boy lets out the string. The wind spins the girl's pinwheel round and round. The wind plays an important role, yet it is not only the wind, but also the structure of each plaything that generates its behavior. The pinwheel's structure can be described as a square piece of material folded on the diagonal and pinned to a stick. The kite is also made from a lightweight piece of material, but a frame supports its structure. The kite is attached to a long string and has a tail. The structure of the toys determines which one spins and which one flies. A systems thinker understands that a system's structure generates its behavior.

"There is no doubt whatsoever about the influence of architecture and structure upon human character and action. We make our buildings and afterwards they make us. They regulate the course of our lives."

— Winston Churchill, Prime Minister

Structures can be very tangible, as with the various configurations of space in a building. As suggested by Churchill in the above quotation, buildings are a good place to start identifying system structures. We design buildings in specific ways for specific purposes. For example, a commercial kitchen must have certain features to make it functional for preparing food. Residential kitchens have many of those same features. They are designed for homes to accommodate not only food preparation, but also to serve as a place for family and friends to congregate while the meal is being prepared.

Desks versus tables

A traditional classroom may be arranged with desks in rows so all students face the front of the room. Ideal for listening to a lecture, taking notes and watching an instructor write on a chalkboard, it may not be the most suitable arrangement if the teacher desires a more collaborative atmosphere in the classroom. Instead, she may exchange desks for tables and replace the chalkboard at the front of the room with portable white boards to encourage students to work together to solve equations and share their thinking with other students.

Wedding etiquette

Excited about their upcoming wedding reception, Mark and Madeline had a serious conversation about whether or not to use place cards. Mark preferred a more laissez-faire approach where guests were free to mingle for drinks and then make their way to a table of their choice when it was time for the meal. Madeline preferred a more formal approach with place cards — a tangible structure that would direct the movement of their guests and influence the conversations that would take place during the meal. After some convincing, Mark agreed with Madeline that the use of place cards would be a structure that would help reduce potentially awkward situations and help ensure that all their guests had an enjoyable evening.

Reflection: Think about a workplace team that functions well.

Effective structures often bring about open communication, high levels of trust and a culture that holds individuals in high regard and expresses appreciation of differences. What are some examples of those effective structures?

Practice the Habit

Let's identify some of the structures found in traffic, as part of a transportation system. What are some physical structures in that system?

- Physical arrangement of roads and highways
- Traffic signals
- Others?_____

How do those structures influence the behavior of the system? How do vehicles move through the system?

- Traffic lights mean that cars will have to stop when the signal is red, leading to delays for some drivers. If these delays are unacceptable, the local jurisdiction may build overpasses to produce a continuous traffic flow at that intersection.

- Many highway systems have installed electronic marquees with the capacity to display changing messages. The message may alert drivers to a specific hazard or it may carry a general warning message, such as reminding drivers of the danger of driving in an impaired state. The variability of the message is intended to increase the likelihood that drivers pay attention to the warnings.

- What are some other examples of traffic structures that influence system behavior?

  _____

Now choose a system that is relevant to you and your work. What structures can you identify? What behaviors are produced by those structures?

_____

_____

_____

Keep in mind that not all structures are physical, nor are all structures visible. Read on to explore less tangible structures.

Systems thinkers, who recognize that a system's structure generates its behavior, are intentional about matching a system's design with its purpose. They envision the desired system behavior and then they create the structures that will produce the desired outcomes. If you desire to change the way a system behaves, you do so by changing the structure of the system. Structures influence the behavior of the system. Those structures can be physical structures, as in architecture; laws and policies, as in government; or social structures like traditions and routines.

Sibling relationships

Structures can impact the attainment of goals. Personal habits can be influenced by structures that either support or serve as barriers to personal goals.

Systems' structures can also be less concrete. Personal relationships offer good examples of less tangible structures. Relationships among family members can produce a variety of dynamics. Adult family members who have strayed from siblings because of geography or varied interests may not talk with one another for months. Yet, those who live close by or those who work or socialize together may be in regular contact. Family traditions may also influence how different families build and maintain relationships. Regular Sunday dinners or summer reunions at the lake are predictable structures that contribute to families staying connected with one another.

Raj has a desire to eat better; however, his daily stop at the donut shop is not likely to help him achieve his goal of healthier eating. The donut shop is currently on his way to work – its physical placement is a structure that encourages his daily stop. Psychologists recognize that to change human behavior an individual, in this case Raj, has to want to make the change. Raj needs to replace his current habit with a new behavior. So instead of driving by the donut shop each day, he can change his route to work or find a new place to stop on his current route that offers healthier choices. Adjusting the structure will help Raj develop a different habit and significantly influence his chance of successfully changing his behavior.

Practice the Habit

What structures are you aware of in your own family? How do those structures contribute to your family dynamics?

_____

When considering relationships, what other structures come to mind?

_____

What is a personal habit that you want to work on? It may be something you want to change or something you want to add to your routine.

_____

What current structures are making that change more difficult?

_____

How could you adjust those structures in order to increase your chances of success with the new Habit?

_____

The impact of a system's structure

Like individuals, organizations such as businesses, non-profits, schools and healthcare facilities also set goals to attain desired outcomes. For example, a new non-profit recognizes that more name recognition could be a leverage to increase donations. The cost of traditional media is a financial stretch, so they decide that one way to spread the word about their good work is restructuring the board to include additional members from more diverse backgrounds. A stated responsibility of board members would be to utilize their own social media connections to build name recognition for the non-profit.

The non-profit recognized that the individual networks of their board members were a structure they could leverage to achieve their goal of greater name recognition. Even when you fully appreciate the role of a system's structure it can be tricky to identify which structures need to be changed in order to achieve your desired result. Changes in structure that are too rapid or too dramatic can produce unintended consequences and take you farther away from the results you want to achieve.

Recognizes the impact of time delays when exploring cause and effect relationships

©2014 Waters Foundation, Systems Thinking in Schools
www.watersfoundation.org

CONNECTION TO OTHER HABITS OF A SYSTEMS THINKER

Recognizes the impact of time delays when exploring cause and effect relationships

One thing that makes the effect of structure so hard to identify is there is often a time delay that separates the impact of strucutre on the system's behavior. Being mindful of the effect of time delays can help identify the relationship between a system's structure and the behavior it produces.

Reflection: Kites and pinwheels are not the only toys for which their structure specifically governs their behavior. Slinkys®, yo-yos and electric trains, to name a few, are strongly influenced by their distinctive system's structure.

Take a minute to actually "play with" a toy and identify the specific structure that impacts the toy's behavior. Here are some questions to ask:

- How do the parts affect one another?

- How would a change in structure affect the behavior of the toy?

- How does the organization and interaction of the parts create the behavior that emerges?

Practice the Habit

Identify a system of which you are a part. For example, a classroom, a work team, a homeowners' association, etc.

_____

Describe the current reality of that system. What are the structures?
What behaviors are they currently producing?

_____

_____

Envision your desired results. What behaviors would you like to see produced?

_____

_____

What can you do to effect change? What existing structures are helping/hindering that effort?

_____

_____

Recognizing that a system's structure generates its behavior and eliminates the need for blame.
So now ask… When things go wrong, how can I focus on internal causes rather than dwell on external blame?

_____

Change can be instantaneous, but it rarely produces instantaneous results.
Set a timeline to reassess progress toward achieving your desired result.

_____

WHAT'S NEXT?

Complex cause and effect relationships are often circular, meaning that the effect comes back around and impacts the cause. Systems thinkers use causal loops as a visual tool to represent complex cause and effect relationships. Understanding how the structure of the system drives its behavior can help you recognize the complex nature of cause and effect.

Identifies the circular nature of complex cause and effect relationships

When observing the natural world, cause and effect relationships are all around us. The essential relationship between bees and flowers show how one needs the other in order to survive. Bees cause flowers to reproduce and grow through pollination of the flower, and bees depend on the nectar of flowers as a food source. This interdependency is just one example of the vast number of causal relationships that help define our world.

Causal loop diagrams

Systems thinkers use visual drawing tools called "causal loop diagrams" to show the causal relationships that exist between elements. In the flower-bee-arrows picture to the left, both the bee and the flower represent the elements of the causal loop. Because the elements can change over time (number of bees or flowers) they are also commonly referred to as variables. Causal loop diagrams (CLDs) use arrows drawn between elements or variables to illustrate causality. To create such a diagram, begin drawing the arrow from the cause and then point the arrowhead to the effect. When using the loops to explain relationships, the circular shape helps you see how there is no one beginning or end to the causal story. The story continues as you talk around the loop multiple times.

Consider the saying,

Do unto others as you would have others do unto you.

This saying can be represented as a causal loop. The loop explains that the way you treat others impacts the way others treat you. And the way others treat you affects the way you treat others.

To be more specific, if you were to choose *kindness* as a way of treating others, then if you are kind, hopefully people will be kind to you, and when people are kind to you, you share kind gestures with others.

Much like a snowball increases in size every time it rotates as it travels down a hill, the variables in this loop increase as the story continues to be told around the loop. This causal relationship grows with every pass around the circle.

Because these two loop variables reinforce each other or cause one another to grow in this story, this type of causal loop is called "reinforcing." Notice the "R" in the center of the loop that labels it as a *reinforcing loop*. The variables in this loop reinforce one another in a direct way.

When a loop shows reinforcing growth, it is important to realize that the growth is not always considered a "good" thing. For example, if I were to mistreat people, then others may mistreat me, which would cause me to further mistreat others. This is still a reinforcing relationship, although not a desireable life situation.

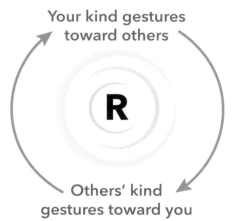

Practice the Habit

Simple Loop Exercises

"Seeing is believing" is a common cause and effect phrase. Draw a simple loop that illustrates the meaning of this phrase. *Hint: Seeing is believing, and believing is based on what one sees.*

Tell the story of your loop using a context that makes sense to you. For example, "When I actually see expected gains in our quarterly financial report, I will believe that this new approach to marketing is the way to go. As my belief in the power of this new approach grows, my hope for our continued financial gains will also grow."

_____

_____

_____

_____

_____

_____

Reinforcing playground problems

Three first grade boys were having ongoing problems getting along on the playground at school. As they were talking about what typically happens when their problems escalate, they realized that each of them was contributing to the growing level of unkind behaviors and hurt feelings.

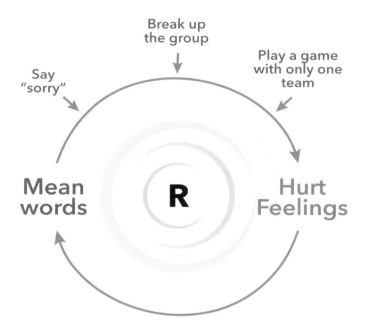

Because these children had experience with systems thinking Habits and tools, they were able to draw a causal loop on a piece of paper and name it "reinforcing." The "R" in the middle of the loop labels the loop as "reinforcing." The loop drawing helped them look at the problem objectively with minimal emotion and gave them an opportunity to discuss and brainstorm solutions.[1]

They realized that actions to try to break the loop were only temporary, solutions like saying "sorry" or playing together as one team. They discovered that the only effective resolution was to use nice words to generate nice feelings, which shifted the reinforcing loop to one that was desirable based on kind interactions.

Balancing hunger

Another simple day-to-day example is to think about your changing level of hunger throughout the day. Hunger causes you to want to eat. When you eat, your hunger level can subside, which causes your hunger levels to decrease. When hunger levels decrease there is a slow-down in eating.

Best practice is to talk through the causal links in the loop at least two times. Begin with one variable and explain what occurs when that variable changes.

For example,
First time around the loop:
As hunger goes up, eating goes up.
As eating goes up, hunger decreases.

Second time around the loop:
As hunger decreases, eating subsides.
As eating subsides, over time, hunger eventually increases.

This example illustrates the second kind of causal loop which is labeled with a B for balancing.

Causal loop stories are all around us. There are two different kinds of causal loops. In addition to **reinforcing loops** that represent escalating growth, which was depicted in the kindness and playground examples, there are also **balancing loops,** as shown in the hunger and eating example. Notice the "B" in the center of the loop. A system can elicit balancing behavior when a sense of equilibrium or balance becomes the goal-seeking dynamic state.

Through practice, systems thinkers develop the ability to "sense circular causality" and identify the type of dynamic behavior: reinforcing or balancing. The capacity to sense circular causality builds a deep level of understanding of simple and complex systems. It influences the words we choose to use and the actions we take. When people understand the circular nature of cause and effect, they are better able to recognize cause and effect relationships and anticipate the subsequent dynamics these relationships create.

Causal Loop Practice

The ability to identify circular cause and effect relationships is an essential Habit of a Systems Thinker. Causal loops are often called "feedback loops" because the cause doesn't merely stop at influencing the effect. The effect feeds back and initiates a change in the initial cause. Consider the examples below. Draw a causal loop for each pair, and identify the loop as either reinforcing or balancing. If it is reinforcing, place an "R" in the center. If it is balancing, place a "B" in the center. Talk through your loop two times:

Causal Pair #1: Skills and Confidence
Draw the Loop

Causal Pair #2: Stress and Coping Strategies
Draw the Loop

Consider the following variables that could be important to your organization:
- Collaboration
- Quality of Communication
- Morale
- Level of Commitment
- Trust
- Others?

Choose two or more of the above variables and sketch a causal feedback loop. Prepare to share your loop with another person. Use the drawing to help explain your mental model of what is important in the workplace.

A teacher's dilemma

Here is a story of a teacher who wanted to justify an intuition and develop a theory to examine some dynamics in her classroom.

Teacher Sara was concerned about some of her students' low achievement levels, as indicated by their standardized test results. She was feeling pressure to adopt teaching strategies that focused on test prep and other "teach to the test" approaches that would likely cause some immediate improvement in test results.

Cause: Effect:

Test prep ⟶ Student achievement (as measured by standardized tests)

Knowing that increases in results were critical to her reputation and evaluation as a teacher, she felt she needed to comply with this test prep expectation. However, Sara was frustrated because her students hated "teach to the test" instruction and often became bored and disengaged. She began to think about other important factors that she should be paying attention to in order to impact measures of student achievement.

Sara recognized that when students accomplished small successes, as in being able to explain a concept to a peer or finally figuring out a way to solve a math problem, their beliefs in their own capabilities were positively impacted. She needed to look for many more ways where students could uncover evidence of their own learning that made them feel successful. Waiting for achievement tests or end of the unit tests was not enough. This shift in self-belief motivated her students to put forth more effort in their

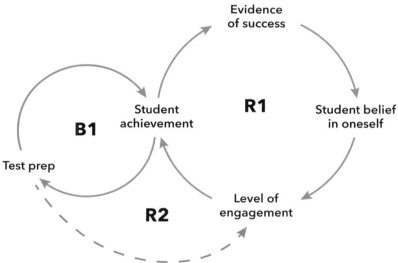

learning. In other words, any evidence of success caused students to increase their self-belief, which caused an increase in their level of engagement in learning. As students became more engaged, their level of achievement was positively impacted. Sara also recognized the impact when students experienced a wide range of measures of student achievement that provided evidence of personal success. She drew the R1 loop above to show her theory.

Causal loop B1 shows the initial problem with the test prep solution. When Sara's students' test scores are low, the need for test prep goes up, which would help address the low-test scores. This loop illustrates how test prep may initially balance out the problem of low student achievement, as measured by test scores. Causal loop R1 helped Sara develop her theory of what drives and motivates student achievement and success. What became evident for Sara is that test prep may positively impact student achievement in the short run (orange solid arrow), but it actually had a diminishing impact on student engagement over time (orange dotted arrow). She saw this diminishing effect as problematic for boosting ongoing achievement in the classroom because of decreasing levels of engagement (see causal loop R2). Her diagram showed how test prep (B1) might actually be working against her effort to boost achievement (R1). R2 shows that test prep over time may actually be causing a diminishing spiral impact on student achievement.

Uses understanding of system structure to identify possible leverage actions

Uses understanding of system structure to identify possible leverage actions

©2014 Waters Foundation, Systems Thinking in Schools
www.watersfoundation.org

Causal maps are also useful for the identification of possible leverage actions within a system. With multi-loop maps, like Sara's, you can easily see the impact when one loop is more dominant than another.

This collection of interconnected feedback loops demonstrated to Sara that test prep was a limited leverage action in her classroom. Her takeaways from her causal loop map helped students discover their own evidence of success through "small win" opportunities. Evidence of success would significantly impact them as learners and achievers. Feedback loops help people discover leverage actions in systems. Sara realized that in order to impact and maintain student achievement, the assessment of learning had to be in the hands of her students and not limited to teacher efforts to increase test scores.

"Shallow men believe in luck. Strong men believe in cause and effect."

— Ralph Waldo Emerson, essayist

Systems thinkers not only believe in cause and effect, but also actively seek to understand circular causal relationships to increase understanding of complex systems. With practice, causal loop drawings help explain essential components and their relationships.

Practice Space for Loops

Employee buy-in

Consider the rollout of a new initiative for your organization. The following example includes questions and sample responses that lead to the development of a causal loop. This example serves as a lead-in to the causal loop practice on the next page.

What aspect of your system would you like to see increase or decrease?
Employee buy-in to a new initiative is critical to my organization.

What key factor causes an increase in employee buy-in?
It seems important for the employee to believe that the initiative has value, so a key factor may be perceived value of the initiative.

How is perceived value grown over time?
Having a quality experience that produces evidence that the new initiative has value would increase the perception of value. So, engaging employees in ways that surface this evidence would be an important factor in this system.

The more employees are engaged in ways that demonstrate proof of value, the more their buy-in will undoubtedly increase. This is a reinforcing loop.

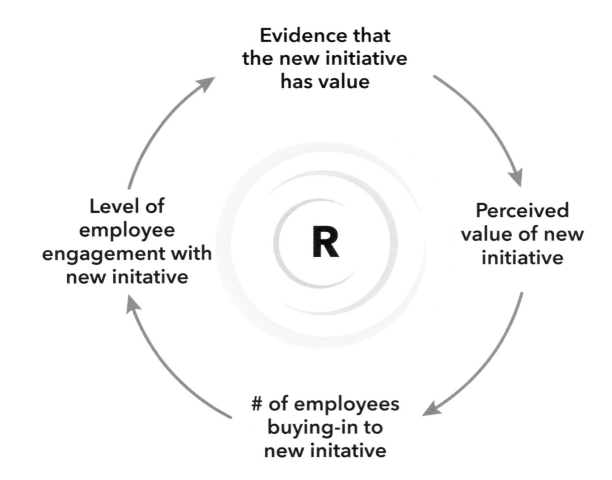

Feedback Loop Practice

The first step in identifying circular causality is paying attention to causal links between important changing elements. For this practice, choose a system you are a part of. It could be your well-being, a family system, a workplace system, a school system, or a community system. Ask yourself, "How does a change in one small part of this system influence or cause a change in another part of the system?" For example, in a family system when one parent must leave the home for an extended period of time for a business trip, think about the impact that absence has on the day-to-day routines of the children and the increased expectations on the other parent or caretaker.

Ask yourself these questions as you consider circular causality in your system. Your responses should help you begin the process of identifying causal loops and leverage in your chosen system.

1. What aspect of your system would you like to see increase (e.g. employee commitment, trust, effective communication) or decrease (e.g. apathy, argumentation, stress)?

   _____

   _____

   _____

2. What is a key factor that would directly cause the variable(s) to increase or decrease?

   _____

   _____

   _____

3. How does a change in one of the variables lead to a change in another?

   _____

   _____

   _____

Make a causal map that shows the responses to the questions from the previous page. Try not to limit yourself to simple causal pairs. Ask what essential elements impact one another in your system. Tell the story and draw the causal links. Be prepared to erase if using pencil or cross out initial attempts. Drawing causal feedback loops can be a messy process as each iteration brings increased clarity and accuracy.

Identifies the circular nature of complex cause and effect relationships

Recognizes that a system's structure generates its behavior

Causal loop maps are a very effective way to illustrate the structure of a system. By talking through the loops you can begin to see the system behavior that the causal connections generate. For example, the loop on employee buy-in shows desired system behavior when there is strong evidence of growth in perceived value of a new initiative. However, the same loop can represent a very different story. If employee engagement doesn't show evidence of value and word spreads that the value is weak, buy-in could potentially plummet.

Reflection: As you consider causal feedback, reflect on these questions:

- How do the various parts of the system affect one another?

- Does one part cause a change in another?

- Where does circular causality emerge?

- Is one feedback loop more influential over time than another? If yes, how? And why?

- Why would it be important to understand the feedback loops of a system as you make decisions and try to solve problems?

WHAT'S NEXT?

In the next chapter you will be learning about the importance of time delays.

When using causal loops to show how elements in a system interact, you sometimes come across a connection that is not immediate. For example, when you begin a personal exercise program, there is a delay between beginning your efforts and an improved level of fitness.

Unfortunately, fitness doesn't improve overnight! The way to show there is a delay between two connected elements in a causal loop diagram is the placement of two small parallel lines in the middle of the connecting line. In the case below, as fitness level increases, so does personal satisfaction, which could motivate you to exercise. But, as mentioned before, it takes time for exercise to cause a noticeable impact on the level of fitness.

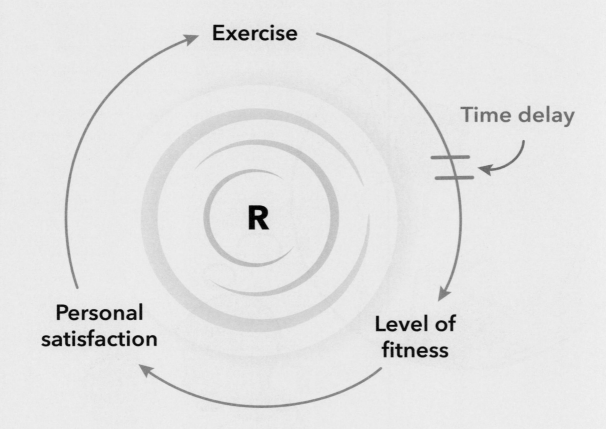

Recognizes the impact of time delays when exploring cause and effect relationships

As the image on this Habit card suggests, sucking on a lollipop could contribute to tooth decay. However, there is sufficient time between eating a sucker and sitting in the dentist's chair with a toothache, so that you may not connect the two experiences. The cause and effect is circular (as described in chapter 8). More sugary sweets leads to more time in the dentist's chair, but the time delay between eating the lollipop and going to the dentist may limit the impact of going to the dentist or the decision to indulge in more sugary sweets.

Smoking's similar scenario

The use of tobacco products is still prevalent, even though the detrimental effects of smoking are well known. Nearly nine out of every ten smokers try their first cigarette before age 18. If these same young people developed some symptoms of lung disease the moment they smoked their first cigarette, they would be far less likely to continue the use of tobacco products. A time delay increases the difficulty of seeing a causal connection between a behavior and its consequence.

When there is a causal connection that is not immediate, it can be difficult to connect the cause and its effect, even when you are looking for the connection. Systems archetypes use feedback loops to tell stories that reoccur across multiple settings and time periods. The symbol of parallel line segments (//) represents a time delay within these causal loop stories. The // symbol reminds a systems thinker to consider the impact of time delays.

The tragedy of the commons

The Tragedy of the Commons archetype, named after one of the familiar stories it tells, is an example of a systems thinking archetype. The commons still exist in parts of the United Kingdom. These historic parcels of land, which have remained largely undisturbed through the centuries, are a remnant of medieval times when people relied on commons for their survival. The commons is land where the owners of nearby properties all have rights to graze animals or collect wood, for example. Those rights still exist, although they are not exercised as they were in the past, in part because at one time the parcels were so over-grazed that this once fertile land was rendered virtually useless.[1]

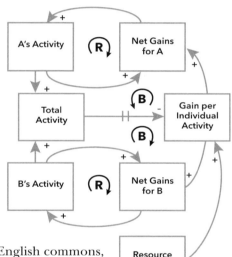

In the story of the English commons, both Famer A and Farmer B are using this grazing space and making significant profit as a result. Total use of the land is represented by the amount of time and number of animals both farmers spend grazing on the common land.

Over time (//) their individual gain decreases because use of the land has exceeded the resource limit, i.e. grass on the common land. As a result, the net gain of each farmer begins to decrease until the land is unusable and neither farmer can successfully make a profit using the land.

Overfishing

Substitute any non-renewable resource for common pastureland and you can tell a similar story about what happens when a limited resource becomes depleted. Overfishing, for example, occurs when more fish are caught than can be replaced through natural reproduction. This is a problem in many parts of the world today. Billions of people rely on fish as their primary source of protein and their economic livelihood. Increased fishing coupled with unsustainable practices is pushing many fish populations to the point of collapse. More than 85% of the world's fisheries are at their limit despite increasing regulation.[2] This is a complex challenge affecting large portions of the world's economy, and its complexity is due in part to the fact that the consequences of fishing practices are not immediately apparent, but rather occur over decades. Once again, time delays make it more difficult to understand the effect of overfishing on the overall situation.

Car maintenance

When using cause and effect relationships to realize the impact of time delays, it is important to consider the absence of a positive consequence as well as the effects of a negative one. For example, we may sometimes do the wrong thing simply because the right action does not produce an immediate positive consequence. The benefits of car maintenance including oil changes, tire rotation and fluid checks, when done regularly, increase the life of a vehicle; however, this good habit is not immediately reinforced, so the absence of a long-term view may delay regular maintenance.

Neighborhood noise

In addition, there are circumstances that won't tolerate time delays. In these circumstances, failure to take action can lead to the escalation of a situation. Imagine you are enjoying an evening with friends when your neighbors come over and ask you to turn down the television. You acknowledge the request, but plan to comply at the end of your movie. Irritated by what they perceive as your unwillingness to take action, they call the police and file a formal complaint. In this scenario, what you perceive as a reasonable delay is taken by your neighbor as an unacceptable one, leading to escalation of the situation.

Time as resource

It is not only tangible accumulations like pastureland and fish that are subject to the effect of time delays. Your time is a limited resource. When you fail to monitor the impact of the multiple things demanding attention for your time, you may find that over time the gain from each activity is also decreasing.

Practice the Habit

Use the Tragedy of the Commons archetype to create your own story.

Imagine that the resource is your time, which you can choose to measure in hours per day, energy, or attention. In the boxes Activity A and Activity B, place things that are important to you and take significant amounts of time. For example, work, parenting, fitness, hobbies, etc. Describe for yourself the benefits you receive from those activities. Consider how that creates reinforcing feedback, causing you to do more of the initial activities.

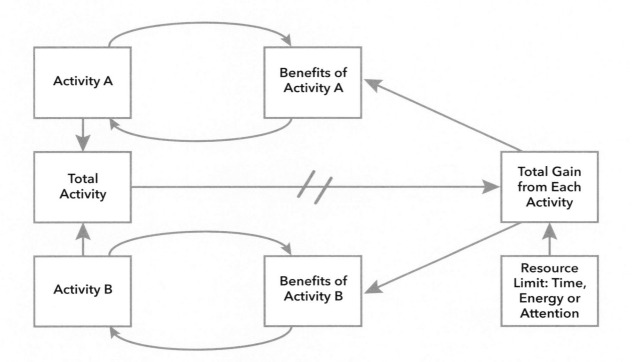

Use these questions to help you complete the diagram:

- What is the overall benefit that you are receiving? (It could be something like personal fulfillment, financial stability or improved physical condition.)
- Over time, how do the limits of your time affect the benefit you gain from the individual activities?
- How does the total time spent impact your overall performance and sense of well-being?
- As you draw from the "resource limit" stock that is your time, what is the impact on the activities you have identified?
- Are there subtle changes you could make to improve how you are using the resource of time?

Want to take a closer look at how you spend your time? Focus on a single aspect of your use of time, for instance, time spent at work. In the boxes marked Activity A and Activity B (you may need to add boxes Activity C, Activity D, etc.), identify specific aspects of your job that demand your time and attention. For example, managing personnel, responding to email, accounting, etc. Then proceed with the reflection questions in the above exercise. Be certain to recognize that the accumulation of these effects grows over time.

Immediate improvements

Immediate improvements are often the desired result of any new program or innovation. As a result, some great ideas are lost because decisions are made without allowing for a time delay between the innovation and the assessment of results. When in fact, innovation often results in a "performance dip," which is the period at the beginning of a major change when people are learning how to do something new and performance may actually go down.

Stepping back to move forward

When companies merge, they usually do so to increase profits; however, the increase in profits may not always be immediately apparent. For example, when two airlines come together, there are many considerations. The newly merged company has to determine correct staffing, meld the two mileage rewards programs, and establish new routes. In most cases there will be significant time delays before the desired increase in profits is fully realized. In some cases the costs associated with the merger may actually cause a short-term decrease in the airline's profitability. This delay does not dissuade companies from merging but rather is an expected part of doing business. It increases the need to monitor the trends affecting profitability and make the appropriate adjustments along the way.

Checks results and changes actions if needed: "successive approximation"

©2014 Waters Foundation, Systems Thinking in Schools
www.watersfoundation.org

A systems thinker recognizes the need to monitor the results, considering the impact of time delays and making minor adjustments before throwing out a potentially valuable idea. In chapter 14, you will learn that a systems thinker checks results and changes actions if needed. This is a Habit known as "successive approximation." When you practice successive approximation you not only recognize time delays, you better appreciate the information you can glean and the adjustments you can make.

Practice the Habit

Identify a possible policy change or innovation that could impact a system of interest.

How might this Habit affect your implementation of a policy change or innovation to your system?

_____

_____

_____

If we make a change to the system, how long before we see the results that we desire? If we stop doing something, how long before we can expect to see the negative consequences decline or abate?

_____

What will be the role of time delays in the effects we expect to see?

_____

What can we do to mitigate the effect of these time delays? Perhaps we need to explicitly make people aware of the potential time delays so they can plan for them and/or implement temporary measures that will allow for the time delays.

_____

_____

_____

Will the change we propose show immediate results or will we need to wait to see improvement? If we need to wait, how long is the anticipated wait?

_____

_____

WHAT'S NEXT?

In the next chapter you will explore how a systems thinker looks for long-term, short-term and unintended consequences. When you fail to recognize time delays, it can be more difficult to anticipate consequences of actions. You will also have the opportunity to learn about another systems archetype, "Fixes that Backfire."

Considers short-term, long-term and unintended consequences of actions

Have you found yourself wavering while deciding between the value of saving some extra cash or spontaneously spending it on a whim that would bring short-term pleasure? The consequences of each can, and perhaps should, be weighed and measured. A child holds his allowance and pauses to decide between the immediate gratification of a sweet treat and the long-term satisfaction of savings that have been building over time. Should I spend or save? Should I reward myself with a short-term treat or delay gratification, knowing that the long-term benefits of saving will serve me well?

The practice of anticipating consequences, both short and long-term, helps minimize the chances of decisions backfiring and producing ill effects. Taking time to anticipate consequences can minimize the unintended consequences that will occur.

The famous "Marshmallow test" with young children, conducted by Stanford psychologists Walter Mischel and Ebbe B. Ebbesen, drew important conclusions regarding delayed gratification and immediate rewards. The researchers found that preschool children who delayed the gratification of immediately taking and eating a marshmallow were described more than 10 years later as adolescents who were significantly more competent in a number of areas. In a later study, they were even found to have higher SAT scores than the instantaneous marshmallow-eaters.

Another way to look at short and long-term consequences comes from the often-used phrase, "Short-term pain for long-term gain."

Everyday examples

 WELL-BEING: Should you invest in the time it takes to exercise and build fitness for the long-term health benefits, or should you invest that time at work, securing a good job with health insurance?

 SCHOOL: Should you consider benefits and trade-offs of the cost and time of pursuing an advanced university degree or professional credential?

 FAMILY: Would a quick text message resolve a misunderstanding, or is it better to make a phone call which would take more time?

 WORKPLACE: How much time should you invest in building relationships with your clients? It may seem like a burden in the short-run, but what long-term benefits will those quality relationships bring your in the future?

 COMMUNITY: How does the use of plastic bags versus reusable bags to package groceries impact our environment?

"Without reflection, we go blindly on our way, creating more unintended consequences, and failing to achieve anything useful."
— Margaret Wheatley, author

In addition to the consideration of short and long-term consequences of the actions you take, do you also consider the unintended consequences of your decisions? Carefully thinking through possible consequences of decisions is a day-to-day habit of systems thinkers.

Reflection: Taking the necessary time to reflect on consequences of action will involve questions like the following:

• Who will be impacted by this action?

• What possible results, both desirable and undesirable, will we see from this decision?

The messy room: short-term gain leading to long-term pain

A young mother insists that her two children clean their room before going outside to play. Weighing the drudgery of cleaning and the excitement of meeting their friends outside, the children make a plan. Without the mother watching, the children quickly sweep clothes, toys and books under the bed, creating an open space that appears orderly and clean. Seemingly proud of their accomplishment, they call on their mother for an inspection.

With an initial nod of approval combined with skepticism based on the record-setting cleaning time, the mother allows her eager children to go outside to play. It doesn't take long for the mother to realize that the closet and shelves are mostly bare. A quick check under the beds reveals the foiled plot. The children now have consequences much more costly than the time it would have taken them to clean their room properly in the first place. They have to endure the added consequences of not being allowed outside to play and extra cleaning duties for a week. This is an example of the systems archetype "Fixes that Backfire."

The children's problem was that the desire to play outside is disrupted because of time needed for cleaning their room. The quick fix was shoving everything under the beds. What they had not considered was the unintended consequences of an angry mother, a bigger mess that would actually take them more time in the long run to arrange and organize, and extra cleaning duties as a consequence for their original deception.

We are constantly faced with the consequences of our day-to-day decisions. Staying one step ahead by asking reflective questions and imagining possible consequences is the practiced Habit of a Systems Thinker.

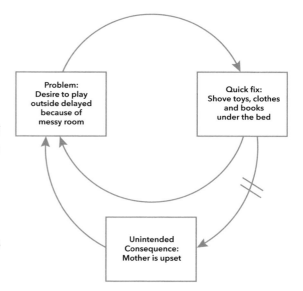

Practice the Habit

The causal map that illustrates the unintended consequences the children faced when they were asked to clean their room is a causal loop archetype called **Fixes that Backfire**. Causal loop archetypes tell common stories that are relevant to a wide range of contexts. **Fixes that Backfire** is just one of many causal loop archetypes.[1]

Think of an issue in which you are weighing possible solutions.

Use the Fixes that Backfire template below and identify the following:

- Problem symptom
- Possible quick fixes that would make the symptom go away (at least temporarily)
- Unintended consequences that would backfire by increasing the problem symptom
  (Notice the time delay symbol between the Quick Fix and Unintended Consequence.)

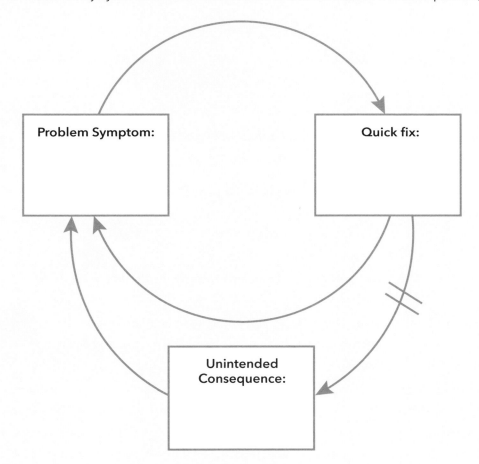

Tell the story of your Fixes that Backfire:

_____

_____

_____

Hiring a new employee

Systems thinkers consider multiple factors when making decisions and taking action. Some people make T-charts to weigh benefits and trade-offs of actions. Oftentimes this strategy is very effective for analyzing short-term consequences of decisions. For example, Judy has to consider the option of hiring a close, personal friend. See below how she organized the benefits and trade-offs of hiring her friend Maria.

BENEFITS	TRADE-OFFS
Maria has the skills that I am looking for.	My co-workers may think Maria will have an unfair advantage because we are friends.
Maria's experience will help contribute to our company's success.	Maria may see our friendship as a way to give her an edge in our company.
Maria is a quick learner and team player— everyone likes Maria.	Maria may assume that everyone likes her because I like her.

QUESTIONS TO THINK ABOUT WHEN WEIGHING THE BENEFITS AND TRADE-OFFS

- What if Maria underperforms?
- How will Judy handle situations where she needs to provide feedback, give directives or suggest improvement when supervising Maria?
- What would happen to their friendship if Judy had to fire or lay off Maria?
- If Judy's employees react negatively to Maria, will Judy be forced to take sides?
- What other questions are important when looking at this hiring decision long-term?

What advice would you give Judy, who wants to hire her competent friend Maria? If an interview committee hired Maria because of her qualifications, should Judy disclose the fact that she is a good friend? Having Maria as a friend should not hurt her chances of getting hired, but the personal relationship could impact the system, and there may be unintended consequences of this situation. So, asking the kinds of questions that help surface consequences of actions should be common practice among all members of the system. Once the practice of asking questions that anticipate benefits and trade-offs of decisions is second nature, the system becomes more adaptable to changes in structure, relationships, and timing.

Reflection: To avoid a Fixes that Backfire scenario, ask these reflective questions:

- Is the need to respond quickly to a problem greater than the importance of investigating potential unintended consequences?

- Who will be impacted by the quick fix? What will the impact look like in the short-run and the long-run?

- What are possible consequences of saving time by implementing the quick fix?

- Is there a solution that might take more time to implement that would minimize the chances of it backfiring?

- Would unintended consequences create new problems that would then need fixing?

Efforts to scale up

When companies make plans for scale-up, it is important to anticipate the balance between the interest in and high demand for product and service with the expectation of consistently high quality product and service. Planning for short and long-term scenarios should incorporate a wide variety of customer perspectives. (See *Changes perspectives*, chapter 3)

Systems thinkers realize that individual views and understanding of the system are limited, and through no one's fault, incomplete to the point of being inaccurate. Structures to surface a wide variety of ideas and anticipated impact will maximize the benefits of the decisions made. For example, a collaborative design team made up of several stakeholder groups that assist with long-term planning is an effective way to weigh options and anticipate the impact of actions.

When systems thinkers look long-term and identify possible unintended consequences, they actively seek a bigger picture than what is currently viewed. By extending the time frame and widening the aspect of the system that is impacted in the short run, systems thinkers broaden the boundaries of what they pay attention to. This bigger picture helps inform actions.

Recognizing the interdependent complexity of systems

Systems thinkers recognize that there are benefits and trade-offs to every decision. Because they understand the interdependent complexity of systems, it is impossible to do just one thing. Every action generates impact on the system, and some of those impacts do not immediately appear. For example, during the 1980's, who could have predicted the impact of the modern Internet and the role technology plays today? Steve Jobs highlighted the long-term impact of technology by stating, "I think it has brought the world a lot closer together, and will continue to do that. There are downsides to everything; there are unintended consequences to everything. The most corrosive piece of technology that I've ever seen is called television — but then, again, television, at its best, is magnificent."

Parents and caregivers are faced with the long-term impact and possible unintended consequences of children interacting with technology. For example, what are the benefits and trade-offs of children using technology? How long is too long for children to be using computers and playing video games? What age is appropriate for a cell phone? How should children's use of social media be monitored? As children get older, what is the balance between supervisory oversight and a teen's privacy? These questions help parents and caregivers set boundaries, make decisions and consider consequences of those actions.

FAMILY EXAMPLE

Practice the Habit

A systems thinker looks ahead and anticipates not only the immediate results of actions, but also the effects down the road. Think about a decision you are about to make that will lead to action. Read and respond to the following questions to help you consider both expected and unexpected consequences.

What are possible unintended consequences of your decision? They might involve reactions, attitudes, results or new challenges.

_____

_____

_____

_____

Identify the benefits and trade-offs of your decision. How will you minimize the impact of the trade-offs? What structures can you put into place (e.g. communication, safeguards, modified practices) to address the potential impact of trade-offs?

_____

_____

_____

_____

Will your decision involve short-term hardship to achieve long-term success? If so, what is your plan to minimize the challenges you expect to face in the short run? If not, describe the road to long-term success.

_____

_____

_____

_____

WHAT'S NEXT?

Systems thinkers carefully consider the interrelationships among key elements that influence change over time. Their full attention to the consequences of actions and the patience required when responding thoughtfully is important in the next chapter. Resisting the urge to come to a quick conclusion is a high priority for systems thinkers.

Considers an issue fully and resists the urge to come to a quick conclusion

Cars are systems. There are many things that can go wrong in the system of a vehicle. Have you ever been so frustrated with your car that you felt like the girl in this illustration? She has a high need to fix her car's engine, but her strategy, whacking it with a heavy hammer, could cause a more serious problem. Would greater consideration of her options early on actually save time overall?

Deliberately addressing challenges & solving problems

By the questions they ask, the perspectives they consider and the consequences of actions they foresee, the full consideration of an issue becomes a natural, integrated process for systems thinkers. Taking time to think things through and to consider an issue fully increases the likelihood of a high quality outcome.

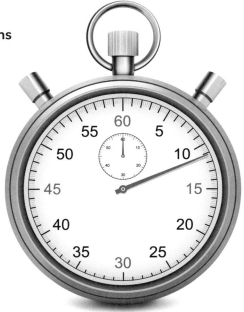

"Fast and Lean" is a mantra some companies live by as a way to stay ahead of the competition. When adhering to this ideal, speed becomes an ally, and taking time to learn, develop and refine ideas becomes a source of angst. What happens when a quick conclusion is acted upon only to create another problem? Or what about a quick conclusion that results in a promising new idea being poorly implemented? Systems thinkers do not needlessly slow an organization down. Rather, they offer a perspective that encourages the balance between efficiency and effectiveness.

In the following scenarios, consider the benefits and trade-offs of coming to a quick conclusion. What are the potential pressures that lead to conclusions that could have benefitted from additional consideration?

The importance of careful hiring

Deb is head of Human Resources for a large urban hospital. Given a shortage of registered nurses, she feels tremendous pressure to jump to a quick conclusion when hiring new employees. The prospect of losing excellent talent to a competing hospital or having a position go unfilled seems to make it worth the risk of hiring the wrong person. However, in her haste, Deb hired a nurse without properly checking her references, resulting in a new employee whose unethical actions reflected very poorly on the hospital.

Deb is now more mindful about the importance of carefully considering the qualifications and experience of each potential candidate. She also recognizes that the time spent thoroughly investigating the backgrounds of new employees saves valuable time in the long run. These carefully selected employees require less supervision and need less time to become oriented to their new positions.

Fully considering the purchase of a new home

Remember Tom and Elena in chapter 3? They had to consider the seller's perspective, so they were not too discouraged nor too demanding in response to the home inspection report. Long before they made an offer and ordered a home inspection, they faced the challenges associated with relocation. Elena was offered a great position at a new firm, but it required a major move. Once she accepted the position the clock began ticking for them to find a home in the new city. However, they had to hold the tension and consider the issue fully in order to ensure their family's needs were met so they could establish priorities for the relocation. If Tom and Elena failed to fully consider their decision they could have bought a home that didn't meet their needs, was in an inconvenient location or was not worth the money they would spend. Sometimes homebuyers, like Tom and Elena, feel pressured to buy a home that is not suitable for them. This pressure can come from an over zealous realtor, a seller's market where home offers quickly become bidding wars, or in this case, the pressure to get settled quickly in order to start a new job.

Reflection: Take a minute to think about all the Habits that have been introduced thus far. What other Habits might you practice that will help you resist the urge to come to a quick conclusion?

Thoughtful parenting

Parenting also provides opportunities to apply this Habit. Joseph's son asks to spend the night with a friend. Responding with little consideration, he quickly retorts, "No." Joseph is then subjected to an extended period of whining, complaining, bargaining and cajoling. Eventually, he realizes there was no real reason for his quick retort and changes his mind, granting his son's request to spend the night. Not only has Joseph endured an unpleasant, potentially damaging exchange with his son, but he has also communicated that with enough effort the child will be able to get his way. How much better would it have been for Joseph to have gathered all the facts first, and then made a thoughtful, conscious decision that the request was reasonable and said, "Yes" from the beginning?

Quick-paced schedules and our own patterns of behavior can lead us to come to a quick conclusion without considering an issue fully.

Improving efficiency

Phillip has been chosen to lead a team challenged with improving the efficiency of a production. He consciously works to apply this Habit so that the team can produce a plan with just the right amount of time devoted to reaching an optimal solution. Too much deliberation can frustrate individuals causing the quality of his team's thinking to decrease. On the other hand, he wants to assure that his team is not just agreeing all the time solely for the purpose of avoiding conflict, as this too could prevent them from arriving at the best solutions.

When systems thinkers apply the proper balance between quick fixes and carefully considered solutions, they are more likely to arrive at actions that achieve desirable outcomes. There are occasions when decisions are time-dependent and have to be made quickly. It may be an issue of safety or a topic about which stakeholders have already debated the benefits and trade-offs repeatedly with little result. In those instances, a skillful leader makes a decision and then communicates it clearly.

Reflection: Consider circumstances that would benefit from quick conclusions.

Linda Booth Sweeney, author of *Thinking About Systems: 12 Habits of Mind*, describes considering an issue fully like this:

"Embraces ambiguity: hold the tension of paradox and ambiguity, without trying to resolve it quickly."

Strategic Growth

Sean owns a successful pool company. He began his company as a sole proprietor working all day to service his growing clientele and taking care of the company operations at night. As his client base grew, Sean knew it was time to bring on additional personnel. He had the knowledge and personality that kept his customers very happy, so he so he was reluctant to hire someone to take care of his clients, even though he knew he needed to spend more time on the operations side of the business. After careful consideration, Sean found excellent employees who were eager to learn and committed to the same high-level of customer service that he had been able to provide. As the years passed, his company continued to grow. Sean established a process for hiring and training new employees. Even with an efficient process in place, each time he hired a new employee, Sean carefully considered the timing and implications of additional personnel. While a new employee allowed him to serve more clients, thereby generating more revenue, it also required the purchase of additional trucks and more equipment. It took some time to recoup those costs and see the benefit of additional employees. Sean successfully practiced the Habit of considering an issue fully in order to experience continuous, sustainable growth in his business.

Practice

Can you think of a time when you made a snap decision you later regretted? What practices would help you in the future when schedules are busy and there is little time to think about decisions?

_____

_____

_____

How do you know when you have taken the right amount of time to make a decision?

_____

_____

_____

Practice the Habit

Identify an important decision that you need to make. Some possible examples include:

- Well-being – analyzing the pros and cons of various health insurance plans
- Family – selecting the best long-term care options for an elderly parent
- Work – when to address an uncooperative co-worker
- School – choosing a college or preschool
- Community – how to vote on an upcoming ballot measure

1. What is the decision that needs to be made?

_____

2. What is the timeline for making the decision?

_____

3. Is the timeline reasonable? What are the potential consequences of acting too quickly? What are the potential consequences if the decision is delayed?

_____

4. How can you manage the tension that may arise if the issue is not resolved immediately?

_____

_____

5. What are the different perspectives that need to be taken into account when making this decision?

_____

6. How can you help yourself and others be patient while living with an unresolved decision?

_____

_____

WHAT'S NEXT?

An additional way to consider an issue fully is to map the system or create a visual picture of the system. In the next chapter you will learn how a systems thinker uses accumulations and their rates of change to create a visual picture of the system.

Pays attention to accumulations and their rates of change

©2014 Waters Foundation, Systems Thinking in Schools
www.watersfoundation.org

Pays attention to accumulations and their rates of change

What factors are affecting the changing water level in this birdbath? If we consider the water as the accumulation in this system, the water level is being affected by several factors including the inflow from the hose, the heat from the sun resulting in evaporation, the droplets splashing over the side of the birdbath and the birds taking water away by drinking.

Concrete and abstract accumulations

Elements in systems that change over time are called accumulations. Some accumulations, like water in the birdbath, are very concrete and easy to measure, while others are more abstract, like the boy's effort at keeping a comfortable water level for the birds in the birdbath.

Examples of concrete accumulations include the number of animals in a forest, the number of students in a school or the amount of gas in a car's tank.

Examples of abstract accumulations include your changing level of fear while watching a horror movie or the amount of stress experienced at different times during a workday or fiscal quarter. These abstract accumulations may be less quantifiable in terms of number, but the rate and nature of the change can be observed or felt. This type of accumulation is often grounded in perception.

What are some examples of instances where rate of change is important to understanding a system?

- *Your infant daughter is very ill so you monitor closely the rate at which you are able to reduce her temperature.*

- *You become aware of a series of thefts in your neighborhood and become concerned about the crime rate.*

-

-

-

How water in a bathtub can explain accumulations

Like the birdbath, a bathtub offers a great metaphor for understanding the idea of accumulations and rates of change. Imagine that one evening you are filling a bathtub. You get the temperature just right. You secure a stopper in the drain and then you go off to gather a towel, some essential oil, maybe even your rubber ducky. But in the process you get distracted. Suddenly, you remember that the water has been running for a very extended period of time and the perfect temperature and soothing suds have been ruined. Any semblance of a relaxing indulgence is gone as you turn off the faucet, release the drain and opt for a quick shower instead.

This lighthearted scenario provides a vivid picture of someone who is not paying attention to the accumulation in the bathtub nor its rate of change. The faucet represents the inflow into this system. Turning it on more slowly would have allowed the bathtub to run for a longer period of time. More fully securing the drain would have prevented loss of those great new bath salts. Adjusting the rate of the inflow or the outflow allows for management of the accumulation, in this case the level of water in the bathtub.

Accumulations are all around you

Systems thinkers refer to these accumulations as stocks. Money in the bank, books in a library, customers in a store, dirty dishes in the sink, wins and losses of your favorite sports team and level of commitment to your work are just a few examples of stocks.

There are accumulations that you want to see increase, like friends on Facebook, points on your credit score and feelings of happiness in your personal life. There are also stocks you actively want to decrease, like weeds in a garden, business emails in your inbox or conflicts with coworkers.

As a systems thinker, you achieve these desired increases and decreases by paying attention to the accumulation and focusing on the rates of change affecting the accumulation, referred to in systems language as the inflow and outflow.

As you *Practice the Habit* in the exercise that follows, you will have an opportunity to choose an accumulation that is important to you and use the bathtub metaphor to focus on the rates of change that are affecting the accumulation. For example, if you were to choose points on your credit score, this becomes the stock, as represented by water in the bathtub. The inflow (faucet) are things that increase your credit score, such as paying bills on time or earning additional credit. The outflow (drain) are things that decrease your credit score, such as too much debt or defaulting on a loan.

Student enrollment

Here is an example to help you think about accumulations. A school principal leads a school where enrollment is determined largely by parental choice. Keeping a sufficient number of students enrolled in school is critical to the school's ability to maintain funding and keep the doors open.

The principal works hard to attract students by offering tours, holding recruitment events at preschools and even advertising in local businesses in the attendance area. She is encouraged by the number of students coming to visit and the resulting number of students who register for her school. However, the actual number of students enrolled continues to decrease. The school is failing to retain the students it has enrolled. Some students are leaving due to family moves or other unavoidable circumstances, but many more are choosing to leave because a competing school nearby offers smaller class sizes. Too much attention paid to the inflow (students enrolling) without equal attention paid to the outflow (students leaving) results in a decreasing accumulation or stock (student enrollment).

The number of students enrolled in a school is a tangible stock. It is easy to count. But accumulations can also be less tangible, such as kindness, respect or trust. Identifying the factors that contribute to building trust and those that decrease trust can explain the bigger picture of organizational culture or family dynamics.

The relationship between the influences that build and those that take away from an accumulation like trust helps identify why a trend is increasing or decreasing. If the factors contributing to trust are more dominant than those that are diminishing trust, trust will actually grow over time. However, the reverse is also true.

Stephen Covey uses the image of an emotional bank account.[1] Affirmations, compliments and positive interactions act as deposits, while hurtful words, unmerited criticism and hate serve as withdrawals. When withdrawals outweigh deposits, an individual is left with negative feelings and the accumulation of trust decreases.

Rath and Clifton expand on this metaphor in the book *How Full is Your Bucket?* — available in separate versions for adults and children.[2] Their metaphor of a bucket and a dipper illustrates that even small interactions with other people have a profound effect on disposition, well-being and productivity. This metaphor focuses on essential accumulations that lead to personal happiness and satisfaction while also paying attention to the factors that drain an individual's personal bucket.

Practice the Habit

Thinking of all five systems that have been referenced throughout this book, what are some of the accumulations in your life? Consider both those that are easy to quantify and those that are more abstract. List them here.

_____

_____

_____

Choose one of the accumulations listed above.

_____

What could cause it to increase? Identify as many possibilities as you can. These ideas represent the inflow or the faucet.

_____

_____

_____

What could cause it to decrease? Identify as many possibilities as you can. These ideas represent the outflow or the drain.

_____

_____

_____

What are some of the ways to achieve your desired level for this accumulation by opening the faucet, closing the drain or adjusting some combination of the two?

_____

_____

_____

_____

_____

_____

How bucket filling works

Your stock of personal well-being tends to be reinforced in a particular direction. For example, on those days you experience a large number of bucket fillers — you have a great hair day, you get an encouraging text from a friend, you make it to work early and your boss congratulates you on the new account you landed — your bucket is being filled and it is easy to pay attention to things that make you feel good.

On the other hand, imagine the day when everything goes wrong. It is on those days you need to seek out things to reverse the trend of your rapidly depleting feeling of well-being.

Sometimes an accumulation reinforces its own growth. In that case, you might experience a tipping point. For example, if kindness is increasing in an organization, it is probable that the "rate of people showing kindness" will also increase. In other words, when a quality like kindness (the accumulation) becomes pervasive in a community, it is more likely that people respond kindly (the rate). In essence, the kindness reinforces itself.

Identifies the circular nature of complex cause and effect relationships

©2014 Waters Foundation, Systems Thinking in Schools
www.watersfoundation.org

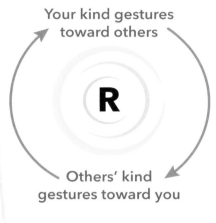

Your kind gestures toward others

R

Others' kind gestures toward you

"I resolved to stop accumulating and begin the infinitely more serious and difficult task of wise distribution." — Andrew Carnegie, industrialist

Who hasn't resolved to tackle the accumulation of stuff in the garage, closet or pantry? These "things" that have accumulated over time are obvious and measurable, but rarely do people pause to reflect on their accumulation of stuff, and recognize that changing the actual quantity of things requires action on both the acquisition and the distribution of items.

Car dealership

Car dealerships are individually owned, but they must maintain good standing with the large automotive manufacturers they represent like Ford, Honda, Chrysler, etc. Many factors affect this standing. Some are very concrete, like the number of units sold and profit earned. Customer satisfaction, on the other hand, is quantifiable through *returned* surveys, which is not as straightforward as the dealership simply making sure it has more happy customers than unhappy ones.

Frank is the Customer Service Manager for a dealership. He works to make sure that customers, especially happy ones, respond to the corporate surveys. His job is building a positive reputation for the dealership from the way a customer is greeted when he walks on the lot, through selection of a vehicle, making the deal, delivering the car and providing ongoing service and maintenance. There are many places in the delivery of service for a dealership to experience a decrease in its stock of customer satisfaction, so Frank builds a relationship with customers in order to increase the likelihood of a positive experience. Successful dealerships look at all of those "faucets and drains" and manage them in such a way that the water in the tub of customer satisfaction keeps growing.

CONNECTION TO OTHER HABITS OF A SYSTEMS THINKER

Observes how elements within a system change over time, generating patterns and trends

Tracking patterns and trends can help monitor a system and its rates of change. Graphing the actual accumulation over time makes the changes visual. The graph can be helpful in determining the effects of the inflow and outflow on the accumulation. Often more abstract accumulations are based on perception. Turning these perceptions into graphs helps identify when the accumulation increased or decreased and at what rate.

Stock-flow maps

A tool that helps systems thinkers pay attention to accumulations and their rates of change is the stock-flow map. Systems thinking is derived from the field of system dynamics, where practitioners and system dynamicists use advanced stock-flow maps made into mathematical computer models to represent a system. These models are used by a variety of organizations, including government agencies and for profit corporations. For example, the U.S. Department of Homeland Security uses these models to assess level of volatility in various regions of the world.[3] Public health agencies use stock-flow models to study the spread of a disease and determine the best methods of prevention.[4]

As you seek to be more mindful of accumulations and more conscious about the factors that contribute to the increase or decrease of important accumulations, an understanding of stock-flow maps could be useful.

Returning one more time to the bathtub example, the stock-flow map would look like this: The main accumulation of water in the bath is represented by the rectangle in the center. The blue arrows and circles show the inflow (faucet) and outflow (drain). In this case they are labeled as filling and draining. A flow represents the rate at which something is changing. Finally in this map you see one additional element. The need for a bath is shown as a converter. It is affecting the rate at which the tub is filling. The more urgent your need for a bath, the more open you make the faucet enabling the tub to fill more quickly. This is a basic stock-flow map. As the system you seek to represent becomes more complex, the stock-flow map can grow to include additional stocks, converters and eventually feedback loops to more accurately represent the dynamics of the system.

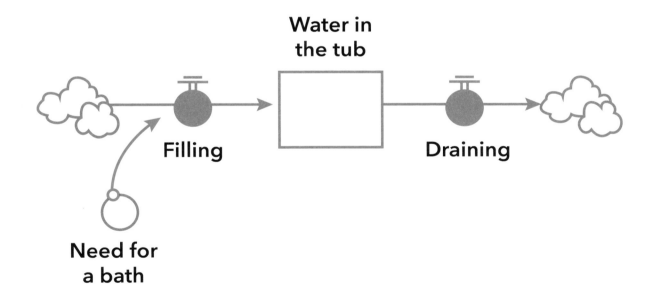

Water in
the tub

Filling

Draining

Need for
a bath

Classroom usage

In systems thinking classrooms, primary age students use stock-flow maps to understand changing elements in systems of interest. For example, students use a stock-flow map to reflect on the health of their classroom garden and quickly conclude that the rabbits, living in the nearby desert, were decreasing their harvest. As a result, they added some fencing to prevent the future outflow from their crop.

Systems can be complex, but being able to map out or draw a system of interest helps a systems thinker see the system more clearly. A single mental model likely fails to tell the whole story. Working together with others to visually represent a system, such as using a tool like a stock-flow map, will be even more likely to help a systems thinker gain new insight into the system of interest.

What is an accumulation you desire to grow or decrease? How can careful consideration of that element and the factors affecting the inflow and the outflow help you achieve the desired change in your stock? Use the exercise on the opposite page to practice this systems thinking Habit.

STOCK FLOW CHART

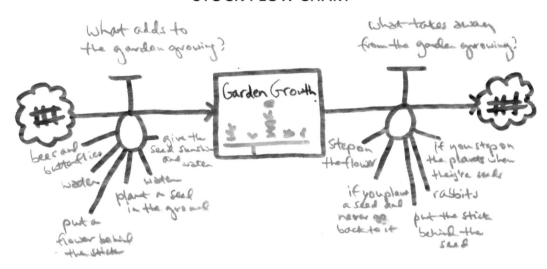

WHAT'S NEXT?

One reason that systems thinkers take the time to map out their system of interest is to identify the most likely place to affect a desired change. In systems language we call that the "leverage action." Read on to find out how a systems thinker *uses understanding of system structure to identify leverage.*

Stock-flow Practice

The best way to practice this Habit is by creating your own stock-flow map. Go back to your earlier reflections in this chapter. You can use an accumulation from your original list or another one that you really want to pay attention to.

Use these questions to get you started and then fill in the box.

What elements of your chosen system can you see, feel, count or measure as amounts that change over time?

_____

_____

What causes this accumulation to increase or decrease? How quickly (or slowly) does this accumulation increase or decrease? What is influencing the rates of change?

_____

_____

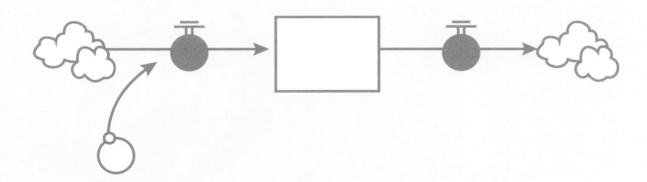

The next two questions are designed to help you find feedback in your system. You might want to refer to chapter 8 for a quick refresher on the circular nature of cause and effect. Accumulations are dynamic. They can change. Looking for feedback helps you anticipate these causal changes.

How might this accumulation impact other elements in the system?

_____

_____

If the accumulation changes, what is the effect on the inflow or outflow?

_____

_____

Uses understanding of system structure to identify possible leverage actions

Think of a time when you faced an overwhelming challenge. At first the situation appears dismal with little hope for resolution as if you'd been asked to move a huge boulder. The ingenuity needed far outweighs the strength of one person. Leverage could be viewed as the mechanical advantage or power gained by using a lever to move a boulder. Yet, it could also be the personal ability to choose actions that intentionally influence people, events or decisions to resolve challenges.

The story of a family vacation

This real life story of systems thinking in action describes a family faced with a seemingly impossible situation on a fishing trip in a very remote area of Mexico. The Weston family was traveling on a bumpy, narrow dirt road, pulling a boat on a trailer behind their truck. Excited to get to their chosen fishing spot on a lake near a small Mexican village, Mr. Weston was careful to manage the bumps with slow and steady driving. With little warning, the trailer hit a concealed pothole that jerked the tire and broke the leaf springs that held the rear axle of the trailer. With a thump, the truck and trailer quickly halted. The vehicle and the broken down boat trailer, now in the middle of the dirt road, blocked passage. There were no services available for miles.

The family considered their options. *Should we unhook the trailer, leave the boat in the middle of the road and drive for help?* As they were weighing possibilities, a car of young local men on their way to work approached the family. Seeing that the road was blocked and knowing they needed access to go to work, they spent time assessing the situation and offered to help. Using rope and wooden plank levers, they were able to hoist the boat off the trailer. After a visit to a nearby junkyard to obtain parts and a borrowed generator and welding machine, the resourceful helpers were able to repair the trailer.

The local men's ability to assess the situation and consider possibilities with hope and ingenuity demonstrated their innate systems thinking abilities. They showed how a variety of leverage actions to address what the Weston family considered an impossible situation could alleviate the problem so the family could get on their way with their boat in tow.

In some cases, a lack of understanding of systems structure and minimal access to options can make it difficult to identify the leverage in a system. In this scenario, the good Samaritans who stopped and offered to help so that they could get to work in a timely manner expanded the pool of options beyond what was available to the Weston family. Systems thinkers do just that — increase their options when selecting leverage actions to address problems.

"Needle in a haystack's easy – just bring a magnet."

— Keith R.A. DeCandido, author

Author Keith R.A. DeCandido offers an image that shows how small actions can produce very helpful solutions to high stakes challenges.[1] A magnet is leverage in locating a very small piece of metal in a large pile of straw. The recognition of the power of a magnet in finding such a small object in a massive heap of hay is the way of a systems thinker.

FAMILY EXAMPLE

Systems thinkers have the advantage of tools to help deepen their understanding of systems, especially when things are not going as planned. Making a visual map of the system can help you identify leverage actions.

You may want to revisit previous chapters that introduce the visual mapping tools of systems thinking, including feedback loops (chapter 8), system archetypes (chapters 9 & 10) and stock-flow maps (chapter 12). These dynamic mapping tools help create pictures of systems and how they function. The added value of these maps is that they are dynamic. The map icons and arrows show a pathway of change and causality.

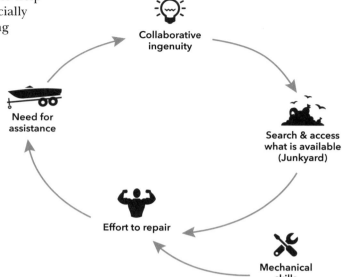

The map on this page describes the family's boat trailer challenge. Begin with the broken trailer and follow the arrows to better understand the conditions that helped solve their problem. Collaborative ingenuity from the good Samaritans who stopped to help, their access to spare parts and the mechanical know-how contributed to the trailer's repair.

The visualization of a broken system provides insights that inform next steps, strategies for improvement and access to resources that may not be readily available. When things are broken or produce less than desirable results, the first place to look is the structure of the system. Causality is an important part of system structure, as the causal relationship between the parts of a system will help determine how the system works. The above example shows causal feedback as the efforts to address the broken trailer actually fed back to alleviate the problem.

Causal maps are effective tools to help make system structure visible. Feedback loops provide an interdependent picture of a system and can lead to the identification of leverage actions.

As noted in chapter 7, systems thinkers recognize that a system's structure generates its behavior. A deep understanding of system structure is necessary when determining leverage actions. Systems maps include arrows to help show how the parts of a system are connected.

Teacher collaboration and school improvement

A school's leadership team was developing an improvement plan based on low student achievement data. The team was made up of a teacher from each grade level (6th, 7th and 8th grades), the principal and the school counselor. This team scheduled a series of meetings to consider a plan of improvement. Each meeting summary included some team dialogue, causal maps and reflection questions they used to get additional input from people outside of their team.

TEAM MEMBERS:

Ms. Prieto, principal
Mr. Chan, school counselor
Mr. Gallego, 8th grade science teacher
Ms. Holmes, 7th grade language arts teacher
Ms. Taylor, 6th grade social studies teacher

LEADERSHIP TEAM MEETING 1

The meeting opened up with questions posed by Ms. Prieto: "Let's begin sharing what is currently working well at our school. What are some of the positives we see going on?" Much of the responses involved the value of teachers getting together to improve working relationships. There was an overwhelming sense that the climate of the school was healthy and that teachers generally liked one another and valued their teaching positions. The team concluded that when teachers spent time together outside of the classroom, they were able to build relationships. The value of improved relationships increased their desire to get together. See causal loop map #1 that summarizes the conversation.

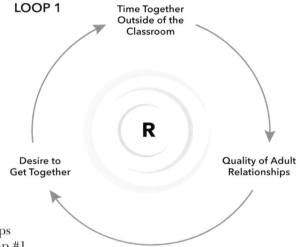

LOOP 1

Toward the end of the meeting, Mr. Chan posed these questions: "What actually happens when teachers get together? What do they talk about?" The team decided that they would collect some information that would help them answer these questions and be ready to share responses during the next meeting.

Reflection: Think about causal loop map #1 and the loops that the team developed during future team meetings on pp. 104–105. How could the loop stories be relevant to other systems?

LEADERSHIP MEETING #2

The discussion began with team members sharing the variety of responses to Mr. Chan's questions from the previous meeting. They talked about the types of conversations teachers have when they get together. Responses included:

- How they balance their teaching and planning time
- How to best address parent concerns
- Helpful approaches to developing lesson plans
- Personal life outside of school

Ms. Prieto, the principal, talked about the importance of teacher collaboration and how conversations needed to be more focused on teaching and learning and about the sharing of ideas impacting the classroom. They all agreed that collaboration was an expectation that needed to be more intentional.

The team revisited their loop from meeting #1 and decided to expand their simple loop about teacher time together. They began to define teacher collaboration. The reinforcing loop (R) helps show the value of teacher collaboration and its impact on teacher buy-in to the collaborative process. See causal loop map #2.

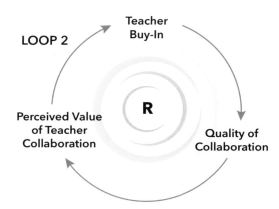

Ms. Taylor, 6th grade social studies teacher, brought up her concern about time, "Despite the value of getting together, there is only so much time available. When time is limited, teachers are not as eager to collaborate, resulting in less buy-in." They all agreed that buy-in had to do with the degree that teachers valued collaboration time. If collaboration was useful, then teachers valued it and bought in to the process. If they found it a waste, they were reluctant to participate in collaborative sessions.

They realized that despite the value of getting together, there was only so much time available. When time is limited, teachers are not as eager to collaborate, resulting in less buy-in (B1). See causal loop map #3. Time to collaborate became the focus of conversations about school improvement strategies.

Their causal map #3 shows the give and take between the value of time spent collaborating (R1) and the reality that there is only so much time available to meet (B1). The expectation to collaborate and the time spent collaborating resulted in a concern about available time. The time loop (B1) caused a decrease in the buy-in and perceived value of collaboration.

What they learned from their map was that teacher collaboration and time available were important aspects of school improvement. They left the meeting feeling like attention to available time for collaboration and the quality of collaboration sessions were key ingredients to their school improvement plan.

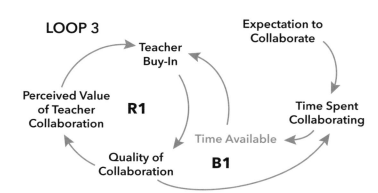

LEADERSHIP TEAM MEETING 3: *BREAKTHROUGH*

The team began the meeting reviewing causal loop map #3 which included both a reinforcing and balancing loop. What was not anticipated was a question from Mr. Gallego, 8th grade science teacher. He asked, "As we look at our map what seems to be missing?" He then responded to his own question, "Collaboration should be the means to focus on the students. Students are not even on our map."

The team then realized that the map was incomplete and that they failed to recognize key aspects of their system, namely students, who were missing from their map and left out of their planning conversation. Their drawing was focused on an adult system. This realization helped them reflect on the significant amount of time they had spent talking about adult issues. Ms. Holmes, 7th grade teacher, built on Mr. Gallego's remarks.

"We left the kids out of our map. We have been focusing too much on the adults. No wonder we haven't moved the needle on student achievement. We just assumed if we improved the quality of adult collaboration that the students would benefit. Improving adult relationships may be important, but we also need leverage actions in our plan that focus on the students."

Returning to their causal map, the team began to add key student variables. This process helped them focus on student work as examples of learning, in addition to instructional strategies and evidence of student learning that were observable in classrooms. They determined that leverage was more about how collaboration should inspire change in the classroom. See causal loop map #4. This revised map was only the beginning. In subsequent meetings, they decided to involve students in the modification and ongoing development of the map. They realized that students should be involved in the process of "seeing system structure." The addition of student voice eventually became a key aspect of leverage in their school improvement plan.

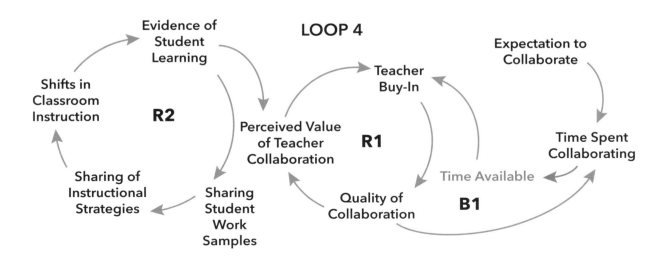

Other ways to look for leverage

In addition to the recognition of what and who might be missing, visual maps can also help identify areas of impact and places to look for leverage. When looking at a causal map, there are a number of strategies to help identify areas of leverage and ways to intervene in a system.

- Look for loops that are friends and foes. Which loops do we want to maintain? Which do we want to see change or removed?

- Look for which elements have the greatest number of connections to other system elements or the element that has the most number of arrow tails. Consider that a change in that one element will have a significant ripple effect to other aspects of the system.

- Consider how to strengthen, weaken or break a causal link.

- Add a loop that will positively impact the whole.

- Periodically ask what is missing. What have we not yet considered?

Reflection: As you consider the mapping process the school leadership team used to increase their understanding of their system so that they could identify areas of leverage, how do their maps, insights and leverage actions apply to a corporate setting, government agency or any other system seeking improvement?

Production cost

The following example does not explicitly use causal loops to map system structure and highlight areas of leverage. As you read through this scenario, try to practice by drawing a loop or two describing this team's process for addressing a company challenge. What does it look like when an understanding of a system's structure is used to identify possible leverage actions? This example taps into the various ways people in different roles view the system and the challenges at hand.

XYZ manufacturing company desperately needed to lower production costs, but for ideological reasons wanted to maintain the manufacturing of their product in their home country. Several division managers gathered to surface options for next steps. After a lengthy discussion about the desire to lower production costs and a recap of both financial and operational conditions, team members began generating ideas.

Suzanne, Senior Manufacturing Engineer

We could invest in advanced automation that would reduce labor costs, but that would take an initial investment that we don't have. The investment could pay off over time with reduced labor, but our employee morale could suffer because of lay-offs.

Gabe, Director of Manufacturing Operations

Another option would be to look for ways to trim production time, but the trade-off could jeopardize product quality. Cutting corners that impact the quality of our product could result in dissatisfied customers and over time decrease demand for our products.

Hector, Productions Manager

We could research the use of less expensive materials, which could save costs but impact product quality. This strategy could generate the same results as cutting production time. It is important that we maintain product quality.

Daniel, Product Distribution and Warehouse Supervisor

Careful consideration of the system that produces our product is one way to go, but what if XYZ focuses on eliminating nonessential steps in packaging of products? We could save some money post-production by altering packaging and distribution practices. With a little research I think we could streamline costs at this backend stage without sacrificing product quality or delivery time.

The management team appreciated Daniel's perspective and decided to move in that direction by exploring ways to trim down packaging costs. As a result, the company was able to achieve reduced costs, maintain the current production locale and do so with minimal disruption to its manufacturing process. In this case, reducing packaging costs served as leverage for the company's desire to reduce production costs.

Practice the Habit

Leverage provides an advantage. It is often a small action that nets a great result. Consider the following scenarios:

 Communities are challenged with business development efforts to grow local economies along with the preservation of natural habitats and historical landmarks.

 Education engages in heated debates about the appropriate level of structure and rigor in its standards and expectations for students.

 A **family** struggles with the challenges brought on by the need for two parents/caregivers working, the cost and quality of childcare and the care of aging grandparents.

How could leverage be determined and applied to each of these scenarios? Choose one or more that relate to you, and begin to draw a causal map to help you better understand the structure of the system. What leverage actions surface based on your deeper understanding of the system?

Loop Practice Area

All of these examples could benefit from the useful application of systems thinking tools and processes to better understand the structure of systems leading to the identification of leverage actions. In addition to mapping tools, systems thinkers use reflection questions throughout the mapping process. Revisit your practice scenario and reflect on the questions below.

What aspects of our systems are working well?

_____

_____

What aspects of our system are producing less than desirable results?

_____

_____

Do we have a big enough picture of our system? Do the elements in our map represent what is contributing to our results? What might we be missing?

_____

_____

What small changes could improve our results?

_____

_____

How will our proposed changes produce a long-lasting desired effect?

_____

_____

We may not notice immediate impact, but given time, are there ways we can monitor the impact of our leverage actions?

_____

_____

WHAT'S NEXT?

The development of a clear and deep understanding of the system to help identify leverage is a process. This process takes time to learn and discover, while weighing options and making modifications. The next chapter highlights an essential Habit that further describes this process in terms of "successive approximation."

Checks results and changes actions if needed: "successive approximation"

Much like an artist's efforts to make continuous improvements and refinements to a work of art, systems thinkers embrace change as a process and constantly strive for improvement. An understanding of the system and the goal of delivering a beneficial product motivate each adjustment. Systems thinkers learn from experience and use that experience to improve their actions. This process is called "successive approximation."

"One reason I was successful in business is that I was open to making mistakes and learning from them."

— James L. Waters, founder of Waters Corporation and Waters Foundation

When asked years ago about successive approximation, Dr. Gordon Brown, Dean Emeritus of the College of Engineering at MIT responded, "Successive approximation: Is there any other way?"

As a fundamental Habit of a Systems Thinker, successive approximation involves a willingness to take risks and overcome failure. The process applies to a wide range of change initiatives including:

- The design and implementation of an innovation
- Plans for making improvements
- The learning of a new skill
- Efforts to solve problems

Successive approximation cycle

Adapted from W. Edwards Deming's Plan, Do, Study, Act (PDSA) cycle[1], the adjacent model is representative of the successive approximation process. Let's take a closer look at each step of the cycle:

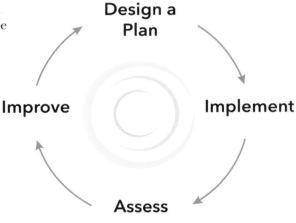

- **Design a Plan:** This is the initial phase of the process. When designing a plan, be sure to have clear steps in place that will lead you to your goal and deliver the desired benefits.

- **Implement:** Once you are satisfied with your plan, it's time to put it into action.

- **Assess:** After following the steps of your plan for a period of time, you will have an understanding of the positives and negatives of your plan. This is an opportunity to review your results. Remember — the "negative" parts of your plan are really not negative at all. Rather, they are opportunities for learning, growth and improvement.

- **Improve:** Once you have assessed your plan, you will implement changes for improvement. A good plan is malleable, and can be altered and refined until the desired benefits (or goal) are achieved. This process will be ongoing, as there will always be room for improvements and improved results. However, if your plan delivers substantial benefits the next cycle of improvement can be delayed.

Key elements of each step of the cycle are learning from experience, reflection and initiative focused on growth and development. Failure should be seen as an opportunity for further improvement — it is a necessary step of learning, innovating and achieving goals.

"Success is not final, failure is not fatal: it is the courage to continue that counts." — Winston Churchill, British Prime Minister

Ultimately, a desire to continually imagine a better product, condition or state of a system is the mindset that drives successive approximation. At the heart of successive approximation is the drive to deliver benefits. These benefits can be for others (customers, students, family members, community members, etc.) or, equally as important, for yourself.

The following examples illustrate the importance of successive approximation applied to design, improvement, learning and problem-solving initiatives.

Driver Safety

By the mid-1950s, the number of U.S. drivers on the road had increased significantly when compared to the start of the decade. As a result, the number of traffic related injuries and deaths had also increased. Engineers used already existing technology (in particular, safety belts, which were originally developed in the mid-19th century) as a solution to this problem. The seat belts used during the 1950s were fastened around driver and passenger laps; fittingly, they were referred to as "lap belts."

Initially, the lap belt met the need of reducing traffic related injuries. However, as the years passed, engineers became aware of flaws in these seat belts, particularly the tendency of lap belts to cause separation of the lumbar vertebrae during a collision.

It was clear that improvement was needed. Lap belts were good but not the best. Engineers in the U.S. looked to the three-point harness safety belt commonly used in Europe. The shoulder harness used in this system resulted in more effective safety measures (i.e. fewer injuries and deaths when compared to the lap belt). This type of seat belt was continually refined and improved until it eventually became standard equipment in most cars. In fact, in 2007, the shoulder harness seat belt became a requirement in all seats in passenger vehicles.

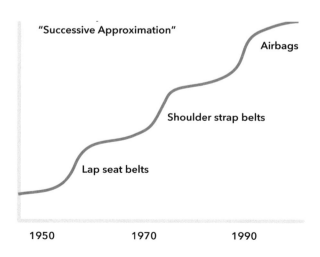

Vehicle safety technology did not — and has not — stopped there. In 1981, Mercedes-Benz introduced the front airbag in Germany. This innovative technology became standard in most vehicles by the mid 1990s. At roughly the same time, BMW set its sites on improving this safety technology even more, and began using side or curtain airbags in its vehicles.

Based on the trend of continuous improvement of automobile safety, it seems reasonable to anticipate that through a process of measuring results and changing actions, drivers and passengers will continue to benefit from improved safety features.

Personal fitness

The importance of getting and staying fit can have long-lasting benefits to health and wellness. Oftentimes, it is hard to get started, and for many, sustaining their efforts can be equally challenging.

For those with ambitious goals, the gap between current fitness levels and the fitness goal (e.g. reduced body fat percentage, improved endurance, lower blood pressure) can be overwhelming. When any of these indicators plateau short of the established goal, people can easily become discouraged.

However, by using the successive approximation process, individuals will not view these plateaus as failures, but rather opportunities to assess and adjust their fitness plan, which will lead to a more attainable path to personal improvement and goal achievement.

Goal setting in schools

In many schools that incorporate systems thinking approaches to teaching and learning, students are provided systems thinking strategies for goal setting and self-assessment.

The strategies help students focus on small chunks of measurable achievement with flexible time periods and available support. Each student develops individual goals that mark gradual, but continuous improvement. The goals can be academic or can focus on student social and emotional well-being. In this sense, the students are partners in the documentation of their own progress measured by successive approximation strategies such as behavior-over-time graphs, as you'll see in the following example.

In addition, students are also taught to analyze and identify when progress is lacking or when dips in progress occur. They learn to reflect on their efforts and implement improvements to their actions to better reach their goal. In other words, they use successive approximation to deliver benefits. In this process, students become less dependent on teacher and parent monitoring.

It is never too early for children to develop and adopt the habit of checking results and changing actions when needed.

"Failure is instructive. The person who really thinks learns quite as much from failure as from his successes." —— John Dewey, educational psychologist

Primary School Dragon Problems

Elementary school teacher Kathy Lohse wanted to build her students' abilities to take on challenges and persist through the difficulties encountered when learning new skills. She used the term "Dragon Problem" to help children identify those things that they wanted to learn, but that they perceived to be too difficult or daunting.

"The term 'Dragon Problem' came from a book I was using with children that helped students solve problems through the acting out of stories. One of the stories concerned a dragon that had to overcome a challenge. The use of the behavior-over-time graphs (BOTGs) for overcoming challenges came up originally with the students analyzing how to tie shoes and what were the easy versus hard parts. That was the original 'Dragon Problem.' We did the BOTG as a group, and then a student worked the next day on his own BOTG because he didn't agree with the class." — Kathy Lohse

In this example, more students became interested in identifying other "Dragon Problems" to tackle. Examples of some of their problems included rope jumping, rock wall climbing and soccer skills.

Students, like Joaquin, used behavior-over-time graphs to analyze the steps necessary to successfully master their "Dragon Problems" and track progress. Joaquin chose rope jumping, and his graph shows how he analyzed each step and rated the perceived level of difficulty.

He discovered that through practice, each step became easier. The more he practiced the sequence he created, the easier

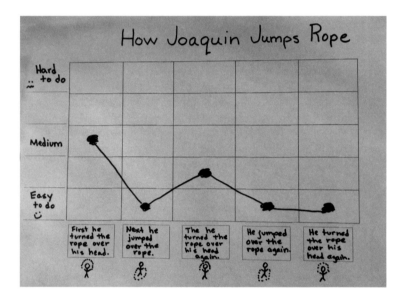

it was for him to jump rope. Behavior-over-time graphs and SA helped students slay their identified "Dragon Problem," so that over time, the initial challenge became an accomplished skill.

The successive approximation process is also used in day-to-day experiences — oftentimes we use successive approximation without even realizing it, as it comes naturally to many people.

The following examples illustrate how common successive approximation is to all of us.

Grocery Store

Many us have favorite food products that become staples in weekly meal planning. Have you ever purchased ingredients to make something new that you have never tried before? Sometimes it's a hit, and other times it's disappointing, but the quest to try new things can oftentimes result in a new, delicious culinary discovery.

A New Sport or Hobby

No matter your age, the excitement of taking on a new sport or hobby requires a successive approximation approach. For example, a person learning to play golf will typically take lessons and practice on the driving range and putting green before playing nine holes for the first time. The scores for each round and subsequent earned handicap will help the new golfer track progress over time. Practice, practice and more practice, along with coaching and feedback will help the developing golfer improve over time. As skill develops, so does appreciation for this new venture. The golfer will make a lot of mistakes. The benefit is learning how to avoid these mistakes in the future.

First Job or New Employment

Many young adults pursue a first job to earn extra cash to help pay for things like cell phones, college tuition and independent living expenses. Learning the supervisor's expectations for the position, rules and procedures of the workplace and required skills are important steps of on-the-job learning. While new employees may not immediately or intuitively know how to complete the job tasks, it is important that they do their best as they learn.

Experience grows and competence develops as new employees complete the probationary training period. Job experience helps young people learn what they like and dislike about certain occupations and those preferences inform future decisions about employment. Ultimately, the more work experience people have, the more knowledgeable and better equipped they will be to deliver benefits to a company and customers.

Practice the Habit

Identify a challenge in your life that you would like to address. Your challenge could be something you would like to improve, design or learn. For example: "I would like to improve my ability to balance work and family expectations." "I would like to design lessons that would motivate and engage all of my students." "I would like to be able to improve my golf game and break 100 for 18 holes."

My challenge _____

What is one changing element that you could track over time? _____

What range will help you measure the change (e.g. high, medium, low; hard, medium, easy; many, some, few; or numerical tracking, etc.)? _____

Develop a behavior-over-time graph to help you track your progress. _____

What would I like to see change or improve?

_____

Time
(establish the units of time you will use to track progress)

What indicators will you expect to see as you look for progress? Or, quite simply, what will progress look like?

_____

_____

Have you scheduled time to pause, assess the effects of your current plan and take necessary action, which may include modifications?

_____

When considering changes, are you accessing other systems thinking Habits? If so, what are they?

_____

_____

Considers short-term, long-term and unintended consequences of actions

As you allocate time to reflect on progress, it is important to consider both expected short-term results, along with those anticipated in the long run. Having a plan that incorporates progress over time and predicts unintended consequences will maximize successful efforts.

If experiencing a decline in results, it will be important to ask, "Are the initial drops in performance caused by a short-term implementation dip? Do we have the patience to work through the dip because we see the benefits that will eventually surface? How do we determine if and when modifications are needed?"

The previous questions will help you practice another Habit of a systems thinker:

Considers an issue fully and resists the urge to come to a quick conclusion

Having an understanding of the issues produced by a system and a keen sense of timing will be beneficial, but remember to resist the urge to do something before you understand what you're going to do. Systems thinkers are patient and understand that quick results are often not sustainable.

The ability to hold tension and live with unresolved issues takes courage and confidence. Of course, there are times when issues need quick resolutions. A skilled systems thinking leader uses experience and the Habits to balance the urgency of the issue and the time needed to explore options.

WHAT'S NEXT?

Now that you have experienced and practiced each of the 14 Habits of a Systems Thinker, consider additional ways to continue building your systems thinking capacity. The next section of this guidebook offers a series of exercises and activities, most of which involve small groups of people learning and working together. These activities offer a wide variety of practice fields that apply to any system. They are playful, field-tested with people all over the world and guaranteed to bring a hands-on, minds-on approach to becoming a systems thinker.

Habits in Action: Exercises for Next Steps

Becoming a systems thinker is a learning journey that requires intentional practice. A good way to start understanding and practicing the Habits of a Systems Thinker is through personal and team development. The following five exercises will help you continue on your learning path. There is no recommended sequence to the practice exercises, and the exercises can be repeated with the same groups over time. Do not worry about being perfect when facilitating these exercises in a group. Remember, the value of each exercise is centered on the conversations and new insights that emerge during practice sessions.

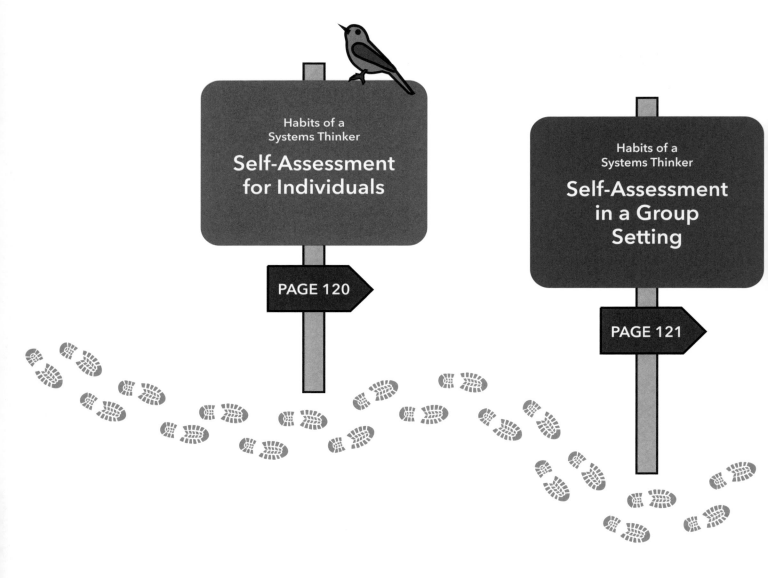

Habits of a
Systems Thinker

**Self-Assessment
for Individuals**

PAGE 120

Habits of a
Systems Thinker

**Self-Assessment
in a Group
Setting**

PAGE 121

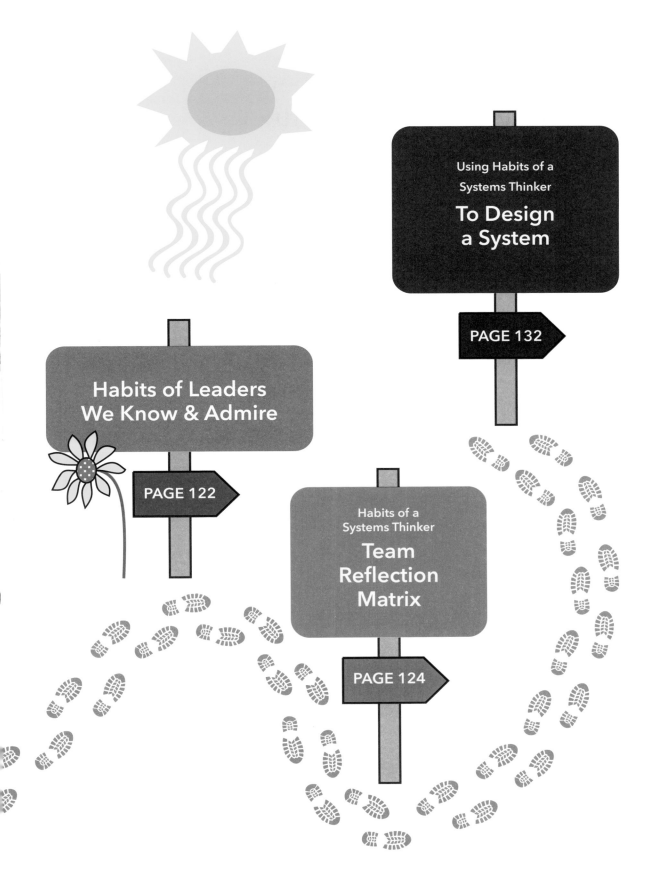

Using Habits of a
Systems Thinker

**To Design
a System**

PAGE 132

**Habits of Leaders
We Know & Admire**

PAGE 122

Habits of a
Systems Thinker

**Team
Reflection
Matrix**

PAGE 124

Habits of a Systems Thinker Self-Assessment for Individuals

PURPOSE:

- To introduce the Habits of a Systems Thinker through personal reflection and exploration

OUTCOMES:

- By using the Habits of a Systems Thinker along with self-assessment, individuals will be able to identify personal strengths and areas that need improvement.
- Individuals will begin to develop a common language as they are introduced to systems thinking.
- Individuals will be able to connect examples of their past experiences to the Habits of a Systems Thinker.

PREPARATION: If doing this exercise in a group, each individual should have a set of Habits of a Systems Thinker cards or have access to the Habits app.

DIRECTIONS: Separate the cards into three piles:

1 | Strengths

Habits of a Systems Thinker that you practice regularly

These Habits are your strengths, and you can illustrate how you have used each of these Habits through a story or anecdote.

2 | Need Practice

Habits of a Systems Thinker that you see as growth areas

These Habits either need more practice or they do not come naturally and therefore need special attention.

3 | Don't Understand

Habits of a Systems Thinker that you don't understand

These Habits have language or concepts that you do not fully understand. This pile is not important for this exercise.

Reflection Questions: Reflect on the following questions and use a journal or the Habits of a Systems Thinker app to record notes.

- When you considered your strengths, which Habits stood out to you and why?
- Were some Habits strong for work, but not as strong for life outside of work, or vice versa? Why?
- As you think of examples when you have actively practiced a Habit, list some adjectives that describe how you felt as you recalled those experiences. Did you feel capable, innovative, transparent, vulnerable, mindful, etc?
- As you identified Habits that you consider growth areas, what were some of the contexts that came to mind? Situations with particular people? Conditions that were stressful? Times when you were going through a transition?
- What strategies or practices will help you address your growth areas?

Habits of a Systems Thinker
Self-Assessment in a Group Setting

PURPOSE:

- To introduce the Habits of a Systems Thinker through group reflection and exploration
- To help teams begin to identify strengths and areas needing improvement

OUTCOMES:

- By using the Habits of a Systems Thinker along with self-assessment, individuals will be able to identify and share personal strengths and areas that need improvement.
- Groups will begin to develop a common language as they are introduced to systems thinking.
- Group members will be able to tell stories of personal experiences that illustrate the Habits of a Systems Thinker.

PREPARATION: Each team member will need a set of Habits of a Systems Thinker cards for this exercise.

DIRECTIONS:

1 | Make the same three piles of cards from the Individual Habits Self-Assessment exercise.

2 | Be prepared to tell a story/personal example for two of the Habits you selected for your strength pile.

3 | Everyone will stand in an open area and select a partner to exchange one story with. Once this set of partners have each shared their stories, they will find a second person to partner with. Each person will then share their second story. When participants have finished sharing two stories and listening to stories from two different partners, each person will find a place to sit down and make some notes about things learned from the interactions.

4 | Reflection questions and small group process: depending on the comfort level of the group, pose some of the reflection questions from the individual exercise and use these questions to process the experience.

Habits of Leaders We Know and Admire

PURPOSE:

- To demonstrate the importance of the Habits of a Systems Thinker to leadership development

OUTCOMES:

- Individuals will identify a leader they admire, and select at least one Habit this leader practices consistently.
- Individuals realize the degree to which strong and effective leaders actively practice the Habits of a Systems Thinker.

PREPARATION: Each participant has access to a set of Habits cards, the Habits app or the one-page Habits of a Systems Thinker handout, found at the end of this guidebook. Place a Habit card on 14 pieces of blank chart or large paper and hang them around the perimeter of the room.

DIRECTIONS:

1 | Provide these directions,
"Think of a leader you highly respect and one who has influenced you. Choose one key Habit this person practices/practiced consistently. Be ready to explain your choices." (See example on adjacent page which may be helpful to share before asking people to begin the exercise).

2 | Once everyone has identified their leader and chosen a Habit, give these instructions:
- "Go to the chart paper of the Habit you identified for your leader and write down your leader's name on the paper."
- "Join with others who chose that Habit, or others nearby, and share your explanation for choosing your leader and their Habit strength."

3 | Debrief
After sharing, note similarities and differences when sharing Habits as key traits of admired leaders.

Reflection/Debrief Questions:

- As you identified an admired leader, was it difficult to choose only one Habit? If so, why?

- As you think of yourself as a leader, which Habits would others choose for you as strengths for this exercise?

- Which Habits would you like to be known for practicing regularly?

FACILITATION EXAMPLE:

Share an example of a well-known leader, like Martin Luther King Jr., and a Habit that would be considered a strength for that person.

The example could be shown as a slide.

"It really boils down to this: that all life is interrelated. We are caught in an inescapable network of mutuality, tied in a single garment of destiny. Whatever affects one directly affects all indirectly."— Martin Luther King Jr.

Ask, "Which Habits of a Systems Thinker would you consider strengths of Dr. King?"

Habits of a Systems Thinker Team Reflection Matrix

PURPOSE:

- To provide a structure for reflection, planning and/or evaluation using the Habits of a Systems Thinker

OUTCOMES:

- Individuals will identify specific times when Habits of a Systems Thinker should be practiced to optimize outcomes.
- The HoST Reflection Matrix will help individuals see the value of intentional practice of the Habits of a Systems Thinker more clearly, and create a plan for implementation of the Habits.

PREPARATION:

Print the matrix (http://tinyurl.com/gr75r9c) on large paper (11" X 14" or poster size 2' X 3').
See visual of the matrix below. Or, on a large white board or piece of butcher paper, draw a chart that includes the 14 Habits of a Systems Thinker on the left hand column (one for each row).

Use a set of Habits cards and tape them as a list on the left-hand column of the matrix. Use the top row to identify a series of tasks, possible decisions, new initiatives, names of team members or possible solutions to a problem. Use a sticky dot voting system, initials, or symbol to begin to see which Habits people on the team connect to the area of focus.

HABITS OF A SYSTEMS THINKER REFLECTION MATRIX

Choose Focus Area	← fill in tasks →				
Connections	✔		✔		✔
Big picture		✔			
Changes perspectives			✔		
Mental models	✔				
Patterns & trends				✔	✔
Surfaces & tests assumptions		✔			
System structure				✔	✔
Circular cause & effect		✔	✔	✔	
Time delays	✔				✔
Short, long-term & unintended consequences			✔		
Resists the urge to come to a quick conclusion		✔		✔	
Accumulations & rates of change			✔		
Identifies leverage	✔	✔		✔	
Successive Approximation			✔	✔	

125

HIRING A NEW EMPLOYEE EXAMPLE:

Consider which Habits of a Systems Thinker would be important when hiring a new employee. This example shows how the matrix can be used when a new administrative assistant is needed. The Habits of a Systems Thinker are listed on the far left column, and the main duties and responsibilities of the new position are listed along the top row.

Ask your team to identify which Habits they think will be important for each of the duties and responsibilities. The Habits that are selected most often will be important in guiding your interview questions and reference checks. See General Directions on opposite page for more detail.

HABITS OF A SYSTEMS THINKER REFLECTION MATRIX
Example Focus: Hiring a New Employee

Hiring a new administrative assistant	Work the front desk	Arranges team travel	Route phone calls	Populate social media	Schedule appt.
Connections					
Big picture					
Changes perspectives					
Mental models					
Patterns & trends					
Surfaces & tests assumptions					
System structure					
Circular cause & effect					
Time delays					
Short, long-term & unintended consequences					

GENERAL DIRECTIONS:

1 | Identify the focus of the Habits of a Systems Thinker Team Reflection Matrix. The focus should be written as a label of a column (see adjacent example in gray box).

2 | Using sticky dots or written initials, ask individuals to indicate important Habits to practice when considering a focus area.

OPTIONS:

- Assign a specific number of dots/squares to initial. You may have heard these referred to as "voting dots." For example, blue dots are worth five votes, making them the most important. Yellow dots are worth three votes; and red dots are worth one vote.

- Give people unlimited number of dots so they can select Habits in any category within the matrix.

- Ask people to color code, with one color representing their own opinion, and another color representing the perceived opinion of the entire team. That way, you can distinguish between people's perspectives about themselves and the perspectives they hold about their team.

- If sticky dots are not available, ask people to write their initials in their "voting squares."

3 | Debrief the visual array of dots to see which Habits have the greatest number of dots and which Habits have the fewest number of dots. Ask people to explain their placements and invite them to add to or delete from the array. This could be an opportunity to refer to the ladder of inference (see Chapter 6).

4 | Plan to revisit the matrix and use it as a group reflection tool. For example, "Our matrix shows that changing perspectives to increase understanding is an important Habit for several of the administrative assistant's duties and responsibilities because it had the greatest number of dots (votes). How will we investigate a candidate's strength in this area? What other Habits seem to be important before we begin our search?"

5 | Create new columns as appropriate and repeat dot activity.

6 | If you would like to see how a focus area changes over time, use multiple copies of the same matrix and repeat dot voting to check for changes and shifts in Habit importance.

ADDITIONAL EXAMPLES FOR MATRIX USE

TEAM ASSESSMENT (EXAMPLE #1)

To assess a team's systems thinking capacity, ask each member to identify individual strengths.

Sample follow-up and questions include:

- Reflecting on yourself as a team member, use your blue dots to identify your personal strengths.
- Reflecting on our team, which Habits seem to be our strengths currently? Use your red dots to identify team strengths from your perspective.

Repeat the same reflection exercise every few months using a new copy of the Reflection Matrix to capture changes the team is making in their systems thinking development.

HABITS OF A SYSTEMS THINKER REFLECTION MATRIX
Example #1: Team Assessment

Habits of a systems thinker team assessment	Pearl	Raquel	Warren	Juan	Taylor
Connections					
Big picture					
Changes perspectives					
Mental models					
Patterns & trends					
Surfaces & tests assumptions					
System structure					
Circular cause & effect					

NEW INITIATIVE ANALYSIS (EXAMPLE #2)

Consider a new initiative that is being planned and will soon be implemented. List the steps for planning and successful implementation of the new initiative on the top row of the matrix. Ask people to vote for the Habits that will be important for each step of the implementation process.

Sample follow-up and questions include:

- Can we identify all the Habits that will be important for each step as we plan and implement this new initiative? Place a dot for each Habit you feel will be most important.

Repeat the same reflection exercise several times throughout the planning and implementation process.

- What do we know now that we weren't aware of before? What are we learning from this process?
- How is this attention to the Habits of a Systems Thinker helping us to be more effective?

HABITS OF A SYSTEMS THINKER REFLECTION MATRIX
Example #2: Planning & Implementing a New Initiative

New initiative to be introduced in March	Create implementation plan	Communicate plan	Implement plan	Monitor impact of implementation
Connections				
Big picture				
Changes perspectives				
Mental models				
Patterns & trends				
Surfaces & tests assumptions				
System structure				
Circular cause & effect				

PROBLEM-SOLVING (EXAMPLE #3)

Identify a problem that needs to be solved. Consider the steps to effectively define and solve the problem.

Sample follow-up and questions include:

- Which Habits must we practice before coming up with a solution to this problem?
  Place a dot for the Habit you feel will be most critical to each problem-solving phase.

Repeat the same reflection exercise several times throughout the problem definition and solution-seeking process.

- What do we know now that we weren't aware of before?
- What are we learning from this process?
- How is this attention to the Habits of a Systems Thinker helping us to be more effective?

HABITS OF A SYSTEMS THINKER REFLECTION MATRIX
Example #3: Problem Solving

Problem that needs to be solved	Define problem	Identify causes of problem	Brainstorm possible solutions	Identify possible solution
Connections				
Big picture				
Changes perspectives				
Mental models				
Patterns & trends				
Surfaces & tests assumptions				
System structure				
Circular cause & effect				

HABITS OF A SYSTEMS THINKER REFLECTION MATRIX

Connections						
Big picture						
Changes perspectives						
Mental models						
Patterns & trends						
Surfaces & tests assumptions						
System structure						
Circular cause & effect						
Time delays						
Short, long-term & unintended consequences						
Resists the urge to come to a quick conclusion						
Accumulations & rates of change						
Identifies leverage						
Successive Approximation						

Pipes and Marbles

PURPOSE:

- To help a group design a system's structure with given guidelines and policies
- To encourage a group to work together, see how parts of a system are connected and persist through group challenges leading to success
- To engage large groups in a low-risk and fun experience that can be used to help them safely surface the challenges that exist in the workplace, communities and general life

OUTCOMES:

- By working together, groups of individuals will achieve success in working through two challenges.
- Through guided reflection about the experience, individuals will be able to voice what contributed to the success of the group and be able to surface insights that connect to other systems (e.g. workplace, families, community, etc).

Group Size: This activity works well with a group of at least 10 people, but no more than 50. The size of the group may dictate the time it takes to complete the activity. A larger group size will necessitate an experienced facilitator. It is recommended to limit the group size for the first time trying this activity.

PREPARATION:

You will need:
- One piece of 12" long PVC, 1" in diameter, for each person
- Approximately 12 extra pieces of pipe to hold in reserve
- 4 rolls of plastic tape, each a different color
- 4 - 6 small marbles

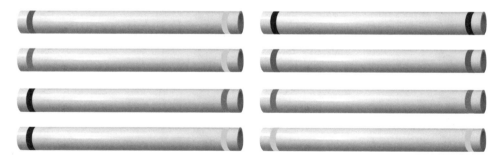

Try to create equal numbers of the color combinations above. For example, for a group of 20, make 32 pipes with four for each of the eight above color combinations.

DIRECTIONS:

Distribute the pipes randomly so that each person has a piece of pipe with colored ends.

CHALLENGE #1

Ask the group to form a continuous, circular pipeline with no beginning or end so that each colored end is connected to a matching color. Reference the game of dominos where ends match in terms of number of dots. The difference here is that the colored ends should match.

Much of the group will quickly achieve success in matching colors, but oftentimes the last few people struggle to find a place where they will match. Allow the group to plan and struggle a bit. As the facilitator, if you feel the need to intervene, resist the urge.

Ask the group, "What options can you consider that will help you achieve the goal of a continuous, circular pipeline with no beginning and no end?" To help them see the connections between this activity and the workplace, you might ask, "What typically happens in organizations that are trying to restructure and align?" (One answer might be, "Eliminate parts that no longer fit.") Reinforce the importance of 100% participation and that no person be eliminated.

You may want to encourage the option of seeking help outside of the group. One solution might be for a person or two to exchange his or her pipe for a new piece with different colored ends. They can access the new pipe from the reserve.

This is a great opportunity to ask people how they feel when they are asked to give something up or change their role, position or belief for the good of the system.

CHALLENGE #2

Maintaining the circular pipeline with all ends matching by color, gradually introduce 4 - 5 marbles at various parts of the pipeline and direct the group to move the marbles through the pipeline going in a clockwise (or counterclockwise) direction.

Encourage participants to try to keep the marbles secure in the pipes, but if any drop on the floor just pick them up and place them back in the pipeline.

You will observe the group using gentle up and down motions to move the marbles along. You will also observe people trying to listen for approaching marbles and preparing to safely move the marbles along.

After people have experienced about four rounds of the marble traveling the full distance of the circular pipeline, stop and collect the marbles.

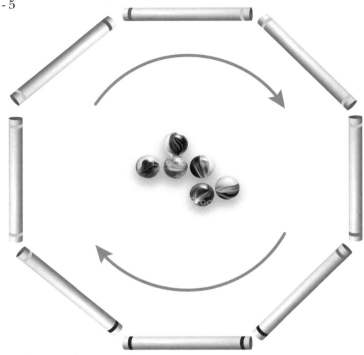

DEBRIEF:

Sample follow-up and questions include:
*   How do you think your group performed?
*   What contributed to your success?
*   If we were to compare the parts of this system (e.g. pipes, colored tape, and marbles) to your workplace, family, school or organization, what could each part represent?

Encourage diverse examples and reinforce the insights drawn from people making meaningful connections.

ASK, WHICH HABITS OF A SYSTEMS THINKER DID WE PRACTICE?

Here are some sample responses you may hear. It is helpful to have either a large poster set of the Habits of a Systems Thinker or a document camera to display the card of the Habit that is highlighted while people are sharing their responses.

Makes meaningful connections within and between systems

We had to think about connections between each physical part of the exercise (pipes, tape, marbles, the team) with other system components.

Identifies the circular nature of complex cause and effect relationships

What one person does to move the marble has an effect on the next person and so on.

Recognizes that a system's structure generates its behavior

The colored tape defines the connections we made and circular pipeline with cracks or openings between each pipe influences the strategies needed for moving the marbles. The tape and openings between pipes were both part of the structure of the system.

Endnotes

Chapter 1: Makes meaningful connections within and between systems

[1] Gallinsky, Ellen. *Mind in the Making*. Harper Collins, 2010.

[2] NOVA/WGBH Science Unit and Vulcan Productions, Inc., creators. *This Emotional Life*. Kunhardt McGee Productions, 2009.

Chapter 3: Changes perspectives to increase understanding

[1] Scieszka, Jon. *The True Story of the Three Little Pigs*. Scholastic, 1989.

[2] Lee, Harper. *To Kill a Mockingbird*. Lippincott, 1960.

[3] Gallinsky, Ellen. *Mind in the Making*. Harper Collins, 2010.

[4] "Elephant and the Blind Men." Philosophical parable, Indian origin. www.jainworld.com/literature/story25.htm

Chapter 4: Considers how mental models affect current reality and the future

[1] Meadows, Donella. *Thinking in Systems: A Primer*. Chelsea Green Publishing Company, 2008.

For more iceberg resources, see www.watersfoundation/resources

Chapter 5: Observes how elements within systems change over time, generating patterns and trends

[1] Andersen, David F., Rouwette, Etiënne A. J. A, Hovmand, Peter S., Kraus, Alison, and Richardson, George P. *Scriptapedia 4.0.6*. The Social Systems Lab at the Brown School of Social Work at Washington University, 2013, www.tools.systemdynamics.org/scrpda/scriptapedia_4.0.6.pdf

For more behavior-over-time graph resources, see www.watersfoundation/resources

Chapter 6: Surfaces and tests assumptions

[1] Bennett, Carol and Demers, Serge. *Single-Sex Classrooms*. Literacy and Numeracy Secretariat, 2007, www.edu.gov.on.ca/eng/literacynumeracy/inspire/research/Demers.pdf

[2] Arygris, Chris. *Overcoming Organizational Defenses: Facilitating Organizational Learning*. Pearson, 1990.

For more ladder of inference resources, see www.watersfoundation/resources

Chapter 7: Recognizes that a system's structure generates its behavior

[1] Churchill, Winston. English Architectural Association, 1943. Keynote address.

Chapter 8: Identifies the circular nature of complex cause and effect relationships

[1] For a video regarding the first grade problem-solving example, visit www.watersfoundation.org/resources/firstgradestudents/

On pp 2 and 71, there are causal loop diagrams that show + and − symbols next to the arrowheads. These symbols can be included in loops to help describe, in more detail, causal relationships.

+ means in the same direction or adds to; - means in the opposite direction or subtracts from

For more causal loop resources, see www.watersfoundation/resources

Chapter 9: Recognizes the impact of time delays when exploring cause and effect relationships

[1] U.S. Office of the Surgeon General. "The Health Consequences of Smoking—50 Years of Progress: A Report of the Surgeon General." U.S. Department of Health and Human Services, Centers for Disease Control and Prevention, National Center for Chronic Disease Prevention and Health Promotion, Office on Smoking and Health, 2014, www.surgeongeneral.gov/library/reports/50-years-of-progress/full-report.pdf

[2] "Commons." Open Spaces Society, October 2014. www.oss.org.uk/what-we-do/commons/

For Tragedy of the Commons and other archetype templates, see www.watersfoundation/resources

[3] "Overfishing." *World Wildlife Fund* (WWF), 2016. www.worldwildlife.org/threats/overfishing

[4] Gupta, Sanjay. "Your Brain on Multitasking." CNN.com, August 2016. www.cnn.com/2015/04/09/health/your-brain-multitasking/

[5] Buschman, T.J., Kornblith, S., and Miller, E.K. "Stimulus load and oscillatory activity in higher cortex." *Miller Lab Publications*, August 18 2015.

Chapter 10: Considers short-term, long-term and unintended consequences of actions

[1] Mischel, Walter. *The Marshmallow Test: Mastering Self-Control.* Little, Brown and Company, 2014.

For Fixes that Backfire and other archetype templates, see www.watersfoundation/resources

Chapter 11: Considers an issue fully and resists the urge to come to a quick conclusion

[1] Sweeney, Linda Booth. "Thinking About Systems: 12 Habits of Mind." *Lindaboothsweeny.net.* www.lindaboothsweeney.net/thinking/habits

Chapter 12: Pays attention to accumulations and their rates of change

[1] Covey, Stephen. "Strengthening families in times of crisis." *Stephencovey.com,* May 2009. www.stephencovey.com/blog/?tag=emotional-bank-account

[2] Clifton, Donald and Rath, Tom. *How Full is Your Bucket?* Gallup Press, 2004.

Rath, Tom and Reckmeyer, Mary. *How Full is Your Bucket?* For Kids. Gallup Press, 2009.

[3] Lee, John and McCormick, Norman. *Risk and Safety Analysis of Nuclear Systems.* John Whiley & Sons, Inc., 2011.

[4] Hirsch, Gary and Homer, Jack. "System Dynamics Modeling for Public Health: Background and Opportunities." *American Journal of Public Health,* vol. 96, no. 3, 2006, pp. 452-458.

For stock-flow practice scenarios, visit: www.watersfoundation.org/webed/mod4/mod4-4.html www.watersfoundation.org/webed/mod4/mod4-7.html

Chapter 13: Uses understanding of system structure to identify possible leverage actions

[1] DeCandido, Keith R.A. *The Zoo Job (A Leverage Novel).* Penguin Group, 2013.

[2] Benson, Tracy and Morrison, Brad. "Other Ways to Look for Leverage" (Adapted from "Systems Tools in Action: Unpacking a complex classroom challenge"). Systems Thinking and Dynamic Modeling in K-12 Education Presentation, 27 June 2016, Babson College, Wellesley, MA.

Chapter 14: Checks results and changes actions if needed: "successive approximation"

[1] The W. Edwards Deming Institute. "PDSA Cycle." *Deming.org* www.deming.org/management-system/pdsacycle

[2] Lohse, Kathy. Personal interview. 25 November 2016.

Chapter 15: Habits in Action: Exercises for next steps

Several of these exercises are also available as apps for Smartphone and tablet devices. For more information, visit www.watersfoundation.org/our-resources/habits-app/

Habit & Tool Index

Acknowledgments

As a team effort, many individuals were responsible for the content of this book and it is likely that we will overlook valued contributors. So, before we even start, know that a very large community worked together and added to this work. We anticipate that many more thought partners will surface with greater ideas continuing to develop and grow over time.

Many thanks to our primary editor, Joan Yates, and secondary readers Alexis Littlejohns, Mary Quinnan and James Waters. Amy Burnham Greiner of AB Graphic Design helped bring our words to life with her artistic expertise in design and imagery. Self-publishing a book can be challenging, but our Waters Foundation printer, Antonio Rodriquez, and The Print Room staff have been indispensable in providing us ideas and superb customer service. Romy Banks, the Waters Foundation and Systems Thinking Group's Director of Operations, oversees the structures needed for distribution and sales. Romy's attention to detail and logistics is second to none for all our team's projects.

> "Your beliefs become your thoughts,
> Your thoughts become your words,
> Your words become your actions,
> Your actions become your habits,
> Your habits become your values,
> Your values become your destiny."
>
> — Mahatma Gandhi

Habits of a Systems Thinker Development

Mary Scheetz, former Waters Foundation Systems Thinking in Schools Director, had the initial idea for developing the Habits and is known for her systems thinking capacity-building work in Tucson, AZ; Portland, OR; and St. Louis, MO. Along with Mary, Tim Taber from Portland worked on the initial version of the Habits of a Systems Thinker.

The Tucson, Arizona, team helped wordsmith, refine and illustrate the 14 Habits and develop the Habits cards as a resource. Co-developers were artist Julie Guerrero and partners Tracy Benson, Anne LaVigne, Sheri Marlin and Joan Yates.

Both Romy Banks and Anne LaVigne were instrumental in developing the Habits of a Systems Thinker app for both Apple and Android devices.

We would be remiss if we didn't highlight and acknowledge the following people who have served as partners-in-learning, mentors and sources of inspiration.

Linda Booth Sweeney and **Dennis Meadows** developed "Ways of a Systems Thinker," described in their book, *The Systems Thinking Playbook.* You will see some similarities between the Habits of a Systems Thinker and the Ways of Systems Thinking. Linda and Dennis's work provides valuable insight into how systems thinkers strive to understand complexity. Their playbook has become a mainstay resource that helps bring theory to active practice and reinforces the importance of fun and play when learning.

Art Costa and **Bena Kallick's** renowned work on Habits of Mind fueled our development of the specific aspects of thinking that were important to develop a sound understanding of complex systems. During the initial years of development of the Habits of a Systems Thinker, we worked side-by-side with Art and Bena to collaborate and align our bodies of work.

Draper Kauffman's book *Systems 1: An introduction to systems thinking* identifies 28 "rules of thumb" for systems thinking. We have often read these helpful guidelines, listed in the book's Appendix, pp 38 – 41, which were collected from everyday articles, speeches and day-to-day conversations.

Donella Meadows, in her book *Thinking in Systems: A Primer and booklet, Leverage Points: Places to Intervene in a System* (www.donellameadows.org/a-visual-approach-to-leverage-points/), offers her wisdom about systems, including key concepts, insights and images that make systems understanding easily accessible.

Barry Richmond, as one of our most influential teachers, helped free us to bring simplicity and practicality to the ways we introduce and explain systems thinking. His brilliance and reference to "system citizens" inspires us to see the enduring importance of this work on future generations.

Peter Senge's book *The Fifth Discipline*, published in 1990, first introduced us to the language of systems thinking. His mentor at MIT, **Dr. Gordon Brown**, was our first entry point to systems thinking and system dynamics concepts, and Peter's language helped us build a common understanding of how those concepts could be explained to others. Peter continues to be a strong advocate and supporter of our capacity-building work. He praises our Habits of a Systems Thinker saying, "There is no more difficult task than to take very complex concepts and simplify them so that people of all ages can grasp and apply them. This 20-year effort that produced the Habits of a Systems Thinker shows that the value is clearly worth the investment."

And lastly, we want to offer special thanks to these school districts that contributed to this work by sharing their experiences and examples with us: Catalina Foothills School District, CITY Center for Collaborative Learning, Hewlett-Woodmere Public Schools, Milwaukee Public Schools, Tucson Unified School District, Office of the Pima County School Superintendent, Twin Rivers Unified School District and Winston-Salem/Forsyth County Schools.

"Systems thinking has provided the opportunity for Twin Rivers Unified School District employees to develop new skills and behaviors to resolve long-standing issues that have historically impacted student achievement. Also, it has repurposed how and why we deliver services to schools and students and the role each of us play in student/teacher success. Without a doubt, systems thinking has accelerated the process in building capacity in the system for all staff."

— Steve Martinez, Superintendent, Twin Rivers Unified School District

FUN FACTS

- Translated into at least 7 languages

- In use by Fortune 500 companies like General Electric, Inc. in their management training courses

- Cited in over 15 texts, including Daniel Goleman and Peter Senge's *The Triple Focus*

"Los Hábitos de un Pensador Sistémico se han convertido en un tema central en todos nuestros programas de consultoria. Hemos trabajado en Ford (Argentina, Chile, Perú) Kimberly Clark, Renault, Telefónica, Universidad Torcuato Di Tella MBA Unilever, Dirección Nacional de Migraciones, Tarjeta Naranja, Universidad Católica del Perú, Linea Directa Colombia, etc. Son herramientas que utilizamos desde la etapa de diagnóstico (entrevistas sistémicas), en los workshops (mostrando y entrenando los hábitos) y en los Coaching ejecutivos y de equipos.

Los resultados son medibles, al intervenir en el sistema, produciendo movimientos en las relaciones causa-efecto.

The Habits of a Systems Thinker have become a central theme in all of our consulting programs. We have worked for Ford (Argentina, Chile, Peru), Kimberly Clark, Renault, Telefónica, Universidad Torcuato Di Tella MBA, Unilever, National Directorate of Migrations, Tarjeta Naranja, Universidad Católica del Perú, Línea Directa Colombia, etc. The Habits are tools that we use from the diagnostic stage (systemic interviews), in workshops (showing and training habits) and in executive and team coaching.

The results are measurable, intervening in the system, producing movements in cause-effect relationships."

— Omar Ossés, Founder, Executive Coach, Taishi Consulting, Buenos Aires, Argentina